To Kelven

Ultraviolet

x

Blue Blagger

آه العابس

×

Heidegger

A Glastonbury Tale

Ultraviolet

Blueblagger

LONDON BOOKS

LONDON BOOKS
39 Lavender Gardens
London SW11 1DJ
www.london-books.co.uk

First published by London Books 2015

A catalogue record for this book
is available from the British Library

ISBN 978-0-9568155-6-9

Printed and bound by CPI Group (UK) Ltd
Croydon, CR0 4YY

Typeset by Octavo Smith Publishing Services
www.octavosmith.com

ACKNOWLEDGEMENTS

Grateful thanks to:

John King, Martin Knight, Paul Mason, Mark Meehan, Walter Otton, Martin Horne, Andy Saunders, Roger Cumberbatch

The Glastonbury Crew:

Ian Seymour, Adam Seymour, Heather Seymour, Simon Williams, Jim Luck, Steve Mantle, Gerry Conroy, Stephen Dudley, Paul McKee, Chris McKee, Hayley McKee, Thomas 'Sparky' Montague, Mick Brown, Ray Brown, Gladys Brown, Charlotte Brown, Jason Manley, Paul Lees, Tony Jones, Davie Brown, Graham Tudor, Hazel Tudor, Fran Tudor, Mally Jones, Paul Griffin, Holly Griffin, Lee Griffin, Kieran Griffin, Mark Langley, Terry Mallen, Billy Park, Ramon Salom, James Docherty, Phillip Callaghan, Gary Kennedy, Stuart 'Ding' Bell, Joe Lafferty, Arthur Sweeney, Jimmy McGhee, Steve Cassidy, Alan Ogilvie, Ray Partington, Paul Smith, Jez Slaven, Frankie Burns, George Skiverton, Sally Renshaw, Jimmy Forbes, Cathy Brolan, Tina Shannon, Daniel Shannon, Baz C, Mark Weston, Pat The Pipe

CHAPTER ONE

I had been to loads of festivals in my time, and Glastonbury was one I knew well. I'd been to each and every one since the 1980s and considered myself an experienced hand at all the trials and tribulations that a trip to Worthy Farm – the venue for the festival – can entail. This particular year, however, would be different. This time I'd paid for a ticket.

Nothing unusual in that, you might think, but among all those who knew me I had acquired a reputation as a top 'jibber' – someone who doesn't like to pay for a whole list of things. These included travel on the railway system (both in Britain and abroad), Chelsea away games (and the occasional home match, pre-season-ticket days) and, last but not least, concerts and festivals.

My dad had died just before Christmas in 1992, and he'd left me a small sum of money in his will. A few months later, when his solicitor had finally discharged his duties and sorted everything out, it was just about that time of year when those with plenty of money and not enough bottle to risk bunking in purchase their tickets for the Glastonbury Festival, held in late June. Using a few quid from my inheritance, I took the plunge and bought a couple – one for myself and one for a Glaswegian mate of mine called Billy. Actually having a ticket for this festival was a totally new experience for us.

The first time I went to Glastonbury with the crew that I would, in subsequent years, usually go with was in 1987. I was with Jade – my girlfriend of the time – a friend called Tony, who hailed from Liverpool, and ten of our mates, a collection of individuals who originated from Glasgow, Manchester, Liverpool and Birmingham. Coming from London, I was the only southerner in the party, but for one reason or another we had all ended up living in the same south Devon summer-holiday resort, and, our home-town differences put aside, we all got on well with each other, to the point that we were practically 'family'.

We'd all travelled together from the Southwest coast on the Friday afternoon in my Transit van, and, being of the same mindset, we didn't have a ticket between us, but weren't bothered by that. I suppose you might say that we reckoned we knew the score, and our mission – an assault on the Glastonbury Festival to gain free entry or, at least, pay as little as possible – didn't worry a single one of us. We were going there to watch the likes of New Order, Elvis Costello and Van Morrison, enjoy a plentiful supply of good quality cannabis, various other illegal substances and alcohol, and nothing and no one was going to stop us.

After an hour-and-a-half's drive we arrived at the festival boundaries, having first been frustrated by a queue of traffic comprising cars and vans heading for the same place as ourselves, a line that stretched a few miles back down the A361, the road that led towards the festival site from near the town of Street and, beyond that, the M5 motorway.

To our left, and from a clear blue sky, the warm afternoon sun was shining down across the fields, creating what could only be described as an idyllic and typically British summer's day, putting all on board the van in the holiday spirit, with each and every one of us looking forward to what we hoped would be a top weekend.

After eventually reaching the main gate of the festival and turning into its approach, we realised that we'd have no chance of driving through. Those we had followed towards the entrance and who had chosen to park in the available fields were being asked to produce their festival tickets, but that particular option was not open to us.

We did a U-turn and drove out and on to the road that we'd just spent ages driving down, but, instead of turning left and heading back in the direction we'd come, we went right and followed the road, assuming that it ran parallel to the perimeter of the festival. Knowing that the festival was located somewhere to the right of us, we continued along the highway and turned right at the first crossroads, and then, at the next junction, we turned right again, passing a picturesque looking cottage and past a sign that read NO ENTRY – ROAD CLOSED and on down a country lane that was as quaint as a narrow road in this part of the world should be.

In those days the festival organisation was not as high-tech as it is today, and the security was not as good as it could have been. In fact, perimeter security and ejecting troublemakers was a job that was undertaken by a combination of well-meaning students, hippies and those champions of civility and expert stewardship the Hell's Angels.

The Hell's Angels had long been associated with festivals and had, every time I'd been there, seemed to have a presence at Glastonbury. They were a group of people that one wouldn't want to mix it with, as their reputation for trouble always preceded them. In 1969 The Rolling Stones had asked members of the Hell's Angels to act as security at their free gig in Hyde Park, and the event passed off without incident. Later that year, and following the success of the Woodstock Festival in the USA, there was an attempt to organise a free event at the Golden Gate Park in San Francisco that would feature a number of high-profile bands, culminating with an appearance by The Rolling Stones. Because of various problems surrounding the proposed venue, including the fact that the San Francisco 49ers American-football team were due to play there the same weekend, the event was moved to the Altamont Speedway in Alameda County, located in the East Bay region of San Francisco. Although the claim is the subject of much contention, it has generally been accepted that the Oakland chapter of the Hell's Angels had been hired in a security capacity to look after the main stage. As the concert got under way, the crowd grew increasingly restless, and there was a violent tension in the air. Despite the fact that several of the bands in the line-up decided to withdraw because of the intimidating atmosphere, The Rolling Stones made the decision to take to the stage. While they were playing, an eighteen-year-old named Meredith Hunter attempted to get on to the stage, but, despite being pushed away several times, he eventually returned brandishing a pistol. He was seen by Alan Passaro, a member of the Oakland Hell's Angels, who stabbed him several times with a knife. Collapsing to the ground as a result of his wounds, Hunter was attacked and battered by other Hell's Angels, and once the beating had stopped he was found to have been killed. In an account of the incident published in the rock journal *Rolling Stone* it was described as 'rock and roll's all-time worst day, December 6th, a day when everything went perfectly wrong'.

The casual use of violence wasn't restricted to American Hell's Angels. In 1980 a judge sitting at Winchester Crown Court and presiding over a case of the attempted murder of the president of the Windsor chapter of the Hell's Angels meted out sentences totalling eighty-eight years to twenty-four members of a rival motorcycle club. They had attacked the Windsor chapter as they slept in a New Forest car park. The Hell's Angles were not a crew to mess with.

As we drove on we came across some bollards in the middle of the road with some stewards standing idly to one side. Pulling up, I jumped out of the van as Tony slid over into the driving seat. As I walked up to the bollards and started to remove them, and as Tony started to drive through the gap that was being created, two of the stewards ran over and challenged me.

'What do you think you're doing?' one of them shouted.

'We've been sent through from back there,' I replied.

'Oh yeah?' said another in a fluorescent jacket.

'That's right. Honest, mate.'

Just then a vehicle suddenly appeared from back down the

road that we'd just driven along. The people in the car must had had the same idea as us but, instead of moving the bollards to the side of the road and driving on as we had done, pulled up right next to the rest of the stewards. The two guys who'd collared me were now not sure what to do.

'Honest, mate . . .' I repeated.

'Go on then,' said one of the pair, as they scurried down the road to help their friends stop the car getting through.

As Tony drove on, I replaced the bollards behind the van and ran alongside the now open passenger door and climbed on board. About two hundred yards further down the road, we came across a similar obstacle. As I had done moments earlier, I jumped out to remove the bollards as Tony followed slowly behind me, and again the stewards manning that checkpoint raised similar objections as those that we'd previously encountered.

'The stewards back there know all about us, boss,' I said quickly. 'Get on your radios and check.'

Sure enough, the 'boss' radioed to his mates back down the road.

'Grey van . . . You know about them . . . OK . . . I'll send them through.'

Signing off and returning his walkie-talkie to its holster, he turned to us and said, 'OK, on you go. We'll move the bollards. Have a great weekend.'

'Cheers, mate!' said Tony as he moved away slowly, and I jumped back into the Transit. As we drove away, no words were spoken by anyone in the van, but the grins that were appearing on most of the passengers' faces betrayed a confidence that was beginning to engulf everyone on board.

Somehow, after traversing the narrow tree-lined lanes that led to the various entrance gates, we'd managed to drive nine-tenths of our way into the festival, past the main body of stewards and officials and had arrived next to a field that we subsequently learned was known as Child's Play. This was an area that was set aside for the countless youngsters that had accompanied their parents to the festival and provided children's entertainers, face-painting, bouncy castles and the like.

As Tony pulled up the handbrake and opened his door, I looked out of the right-hand window and saw that he'd stopped right next to six chopper-style motorbikes. Next to these beasts of the high-way were a dozen or so leather-clad males and females.

'Heads down,' I whispered sharply under my breath, and those in the back of the van instinctively obeyed the command.

One of the bikers – a 'prospect', no doubt – approached.

'Oh, yeah . . .' he said staring at me, doing his best to look hard. 'You got a ticket?'

'Not yet,' I replied. 'There's just me, my girlfriend and a couple of mates.'

He kept coming towards the van. I jumped out and slammed the door shut behind me.

'Here you go, mate, have a go on that,' I said, offering him the spliff that I was smoking. He accepted.

'How many did you say were with you?' he asked with a smile on his face, as he looked straight past me and through the front window of the van. I turned and looked. Some of those who had previously been hiding in the back of the van had heard me offer the Angel the joint and assumed that everything had been sorted, and they were now visible, having lifted their heads to see what was going on.

'Oh,' I said and gave him a look that said, *OK, mate, you've nicked us, but we're sweet, no bother, and we'll sort you out.*

'This is alright,' he said, pulling on the joint.

'Stick a couple quick, Billy,' I shouted as I continued nego-tiating. 'Come on then, mate, how much for the lot of us?'

'How many did you say you were?'

'Er . . . last count about five, but on the road up here we opened the back doors to let a couple of hitchhikers on. They're not really with us.'

The biker, who was in his early twenties and had the eyes of his companions watching him, appeared to want to give the impression of being in control of the situation.

'Five of you, plus a couple of hitch-hi –'

'Thirty quid the lot of us, mate,' I cut in, 'that's a fiver a head for all of them with me, and a fiver for the hitchhikers. We'll throw in a couple of joints and a case of lager. You can't say fairer than that.'

He looked me straight in the eyes. I returned his stare but then fleetingly glanced at his mates. Judging by the state of him, I reckoned that he and his playmates were in the party spirit, and a 'barney' with a bunch of scallywags over a reduced rate of entry was the last thing he or they needed.

'What's the lager? We don't want no cheap shit.'

'It's OK, mate,' I replied. 'We've got some Stella there – hurry up with them Js, Bill.'

Jade, my girlfriend, who was still sitting in the front seat of the van, turned to the back and was handed a case of twenty-four cans of said lager and a couple of rolled joints. She opened the door and brought the contraband over to where I was talking to the biker.

'How much is it?' she said as she handed him the goods. 'We do appreciate it.'

'Thirty quid, darlin',' said the biker, smiling at Jade.

I wanted to laugh, but, as the negotiations were at the critical stage, I thought better of it and bit my lip as Jade handed him the money. I gave the 'gateman' a final 'Thanks, mate,' and we both jumped back into the van.

'That's OK then,' I said. 'We're all in for thirty jib – that's less than £2.50 each – and that even covers the cost of a crate of the lager. We're laughing.'

Considering that legitimate entry, by way of a ticket, cost somewhere in the region of £21 per person and that the £30 we had been charged covered the thirty of us, I reckoned that we'd done well. Along with the reduced rate of entry that had been negotiated, the fact that the case of Stella was one of twenty that had, en route to the festival, been spirited away from under the eyes of some unsuspecting supermarket staff, all in all we'd done very well. Thirty pounds and a couple of smokes. Very well indeed.

'Hurry up, Tony,' said Billy from the back of the van. 'Let's move off and set the tents up.'

'What's the hurry?' I shouted. 'You can relax now, we're in.'

'Let's get going, Joe,' said Keyo, another of the Scottish contingent. 'We'll set up somewhere else.'

'OK, OK, I get the message, but what's the problem?'

Jade started laughing. 'I'll tell you later, Joe.'

For the sake of expediency, Tony thought that a move away from our friends in leather was perhaps a somewhat wise move. As it turned out, we only drove a short distance through a gate and into the children's field and parked up there.

After about an hour, and with the sun slowly beginning its descent to the west, we'd established our encampment. A cluster of seven tents in assorted colours set out in a U shape with the van in the gap next to the hedge that divided the field we were in from the next. We'd built and lit our campfire, and we were relaxing, having cracked a case of lager and rolled a few 'proper' joints.

Reclining in one of the deck chairs that we'd unloaded from the van and enjoying a spliff, I took in the view. We were in a large rectangular-shaped field, and the narrower two of the four sides were at the top and bottom of a slight incline. We were on the right-hand long side towards the higher end of the slope, with the main festival area located about a quarter of a mile away to our right.

The hedgerow we'd set our tents up next to had, all along its length, various shapes comprising camper vans, a variety of Transits, cars, tents and all things associated with a weekend's camping. Like us, the people who'd decided to make this field their spot for the weekend were going through the various stages of setting up camp, cooking a meal or preparing to retire.

At the top of the field was an area set aside for the children. As well as several bouncy castles it had a wooden 'life-size' kids' castle, and near to these amenities was a marquee that, during daytime hours, served as a refreshment tent, selling soft drinks and such delicacies as sweets, candyfloss and popcorn.

At the bottom of the field was a wooden structure that was a larger model of the kids' castle at the top end. We later found out that this was a working shower area – a facility that would bring much solace for many who had either sweated buckets or been covered in mud and filth to such an extent that a good clean was required.

Next to the shower room was a gap in the hedge, which turned out to be an open gate. It was through this that we would eventually leave our field to explore the festival proper.

As I sat back in my deck chair I took in the sight, smells and sounds of all that was going on around me. From our right, there came a pulsing drone that emanated from the bands, sound systems and the tens of thousands of people who were present. We couldn't see it all from where we were, but it looked massive – bigger than any other festival we'd been to before.

In the distance, a seemingly never-ending stream of people was manoeuvring around the thoroughfare system, known as drags. There were people wearing clothes in many wild designs and colours as well as hippies, straight-looking families, groups of mates just like us, travellers, kids, the lot. It looked great.

Towards the top end of the field I noticed a group of people walking down the hill, and, although they were heading for the gate at the bottom and towards the festival, the path that they were treading would take them within twenty yards of our encampment.

As they got closer, their faces and form became familiar. It was the band of Hell's Angels we'd run into earlier.

I said nothing to anyone but just sat in my chair, swigging a can of lager and smoking my joint. As they drew level with our patch, the prospect we'd paid our entrance fee to glanced over in our direction.

'Alright, mate?' I shouted, causing those with me to look up. The biker smiled back and waved, giving us a thumbs-up. Thirteen thumbs, one from each of us, were thrust skywards by way of a reply.

'That reminds me,' I said, turning to Jade, 'what was so funny when we were with those guys earlier?'

'Those two spliffs you gave them, Billy didn't put any gear in them.'

'Well,' said Billy in his best Glaswegian, 'I don't know them, do I?'

With that, everybody started laughing. We had arrived.

CHAPTER TWO

The following year, Glastonbury organiser Michael Eavis decided against holding the festival. Being a dairy farmer first and foremost, he wanted to ensure that the fields of Worthy Farm – the grazing land of his herd of cattle – were given the chance to have a rest from thousands of revellers tramping across them. In addition, Eavis and those who helped him organise the event decided that they needed a year off to evaluate the problems they'd encountered in 1987 through the increase in both the size of the festival and the numbers attending.

The first festival he'd held had been in September 1970 when, inspired by the nearby Bath Blues Festival, he organised a gathering on his farmland which some 1,500 people attended, each paying £1 to be entertained by none other than an emerging Marc Bolan and T. Rex. A month later T. Rex released 'Ride A White Swan' as a single, the track becoming their first Top 40 chart hit. From that point, Bolan went on to become one of the biggest acts of the 1970s. The following year, Eavis allowed the event to be held on his land, but changed the month to June to coincide with the midsummer solstice. This time an estimated 12,000 attended and watched the likes of David Bowie, Hawkwind, Fairport Convention, Arthur Brown and the legendary Joan Baez. In 1972 Hawkwind returned to what was effectively a small free festival, while the next, again a free event, took place in 1978 when some 500 – the majority of who had attended the solstice at Stonehenge – made their way to Worthy Farm to continue the celebrations. The following year Eavis again decided to hold an organised festival lasting three days when Genesis, The Sensational Alex Harvey Band,

Steve Hillage and Peter Gabriel performed in front of around 12,000 people who'd paid an entrance fee of £8. After a year off, the Glastonbury Fayre (as it was then called) returned in 1981 when artists such as New Order, Hawkwind, Aswad, Roy Harper and punk-poet John Cooper Clarke appeared and helped to establish the festival as a major venue on the British gig circuit.

In 1989 the majority of those who'd travelled with me to Glastonbury in 1987 were once again on board my van along with a couple of the lads who'd heard the tales we'd told of our previous visit and wanted to experience the madness for themselves. The acts headlining that year included The Waterboys, Hothouse Flowers, The Pixies and Suzanne Vega with both Elvis Costello and Van Morrison returning for consecutive festival appearances.

This was also the year that the rave scene found its way to Glastonbury with the designer drug ecstasy in abundance, and, once the official stages had shut down at around midnight, at various points around the festival the sounds of 180-beats-per-minute dance tracks boomed into the night, cutting through the darkness until dawn broke with Joe Bananas – a stall selling blankets during the day and located on the main drag – among the most popular of the unofficial venues and attracting ravers in their hundreds. This was the time that those attending Glastonbury could still drive their vehicles on to the festival site – a practice that was, in future years, to be restricted – and, taking advantage of the necessary transport, several enterprising DJs brought entire sound systems and generators with them and made their money by spinning their records, attracting the punters and selling ecstasy tablets by the suitcaseful.

Meanwhile, those of us travelling from south Devon had originally intended to leave at 1pm to make the eighty-mile drive from where we lived, so, if we left on time, we would arrive at the festival by about 3pm. As usual, however, by the time each individual had finished their preparations for the weekend, it was well past 6pm when we finally left town.

Once we eventually joined the queue for the festival, the line of cars snaked back at least four miles from the gates. We were in for a long wait. The Glaswegian contingent – Keyo, Sparky, Gerry and Billy – decided to leave the comfort of the van and walk the mile or so to a pub on the route to our destination. They felt their time was better served waiting for the rest of us at the pub and ordering a pint or two while the queue shortened.

After half an hour, having moved about a quarter of a mile, a few of us who were still on board the van decided to walk down to the pub ourselves. Tony, who had been doing all the driving, stayed on the van with his 'chick of the moment', Lou, along with Jade and Gerry and Keyo's girlfriends, Jilly and Lynn.

The road from the M5 was, as the crow flies, a journey of about fifteen miles, and during the other fifty-one weekends of the year it would, no doubt, have made a pleasant ten- or fifteen-minute drive, the rich colours of the English countryside blending harmoniously with the hues offered by a descending early-evening sun.

During the weekend that was Glastonbury, however, the scenario was slightly different. True, the scenery was still as stunning, but the road, normally so quiet, was bumper to bumper with cars full of mainly young people intent on having a great weekend of camping, watching some big-name bands and getting smashed out of their heads on one or other or even several different illegal drugs.

If those brave enough to have served Crown and Country and fought for Britain in times of conflict could have seen the sight, they would, I'm sure, have wondered why they'd bothered. The queue of cars contained a mass of people hailing from all corners of the British Isles and far beyond, and the likelihood was that the majority were either drinking alcohol or smoking joints of various flavours. The fact that a good majority of the people in control of the vehicles were also taking part in such revelry would have been enough to stir the anger in the mildest of the breed that is described as Middle England. Every car seemed crammed with either passengers or possessions such as tents and rucksacks. Everybody was in the party mood, and no one seemed concerned about the wait they were enduring.

Those of us who'd left the van to join the others in the pub walked along the road past the line of waiting vehicles with the sense that we, along with everyone else like us, were in control and setting the agenda for the coming weekend, and the feeling of euphoria that was induced soon overwhelmed us. The fact that Her Majesty's Constabulary were regularly driving down the road in Range Rovers or on motorcycles didn't seem to bother anyone. They were stretched to the limit and far too busy to bother with a few people who were merely drinking while driving or in possession of a small amount of drugs.

True, they would choose a few unfortunates and make some token arrests, but those who made up that number were generally people who were either taking the piss and blatantly using drugs right under the noses of the police or just plain naive.

Along with the other drug squads drawn from various constabularies, the Avon and Somerset Police's main concern would be trying to deal with those they deemed the main suppliers of drugs as well as coping with the mini crime wave that always accompanied the festival.

The previous year, some 60,000 people had attended. This time there would be more, with an estimated 65,000 buying tickets. They say that the crowd attending a football match is a microcosm of society. The same could be said of pop festivals except that the very nature of rock and roll demands the sex and drugs as well. The sex is a personal thing and is a commodity not easily marketed at the type of event to which we were travelling. Drugs, however, were a different matter.

Anybody who's ever fancied themselves as bit of a 'man', a 'French Connection' or a 'Midnight Express' thinks they'll have a chance to turn a bob or two at a festival. There's loads of trade, and if you're good at what you do you can earn well. The profession, though, is fraught with danger. Nobody knows exactly who's who, and unless you're firmed up with a good crew behind you it's easy to fall prey to the numerous gangs who specialise in negotiating with those individuals who they feel worthy of a 'talking to' about their 'tax arrears'.

Even if the muggers are avoided, there is also the possibility that someone will follow you back to where you're camping, watch where you stash your gear and money, and, if you've been sussed and leave your camp unguarded, you will be robbed. It's a fair bet that many of the big encampments that are constructed at festivals – especially those with vicious-looking dogs in attendance and a few handy fellas knocking about – are the hub of some criminally motivated, money-making venture or other.

Those with no criminal tendencies can also make money at Glastonbury. The majority of legitimate traders selling their goods are located in what is known as the market area, which, put simply, is the main shopping zone and, if an analogy were needed, could be described as the town centre. It is comprised of several connected drags that form an almost oval shape with the traders displaying their wares from their stalls and vans on both sides of the thoroughfare. The enclosure formed by the inner edge is reserved as a camping area for those working the market and as a place to keep their supplies. As well as this ring of shops, some of the drags leading away from it are also tightly packed with vendors hawking whatever they think will make them money.

It was here that many of those supplying the festival-goers with food and drink were set up. From the hundreds of individual enterprises, a menu that catered for the greasy-spoon-lover all the way to those who favoured the more exotic could be found. Of course, there was, as well, a healthy and very good range for those preferring a vegan, vegetarian or ethnic-style cuisine. Drinks of the soft and alcoholic variety were on sale everywhere, as was my favourite tipple, the fresh-fruit smoothie.

Ordinary everyday items of every conceivable type could also be found there. It's a fact that you can turn up in the clothes you're standing in and, provided that cash is readily available, buy everything needed to survive. Tents, sleeping bags, blankets, toilet rolls, toothbrushes and toothpaste. Clothes both new and secondhand, shoes, Wellington boots, washing-up liquid, biscuits, daily newspapers, jewellery, postcards, hats, sunglasses, umbrellas, sweets, tapes, records, radios, cars, vans, motorbikes. One year there was even a double-decker bus available as a prize in a raffle, although whether the prize was claimed is questionable, if, indeed, it was a legitimate competition. Tony, in later years, swore blind he'd seen the same prize in the same spot for three festivals in a row.

Then there were the fields where the various stages for the bands and other entertainment were set up. There was the NME Stage, the Acoustic Stage, the Jazz Stage among others, and, largest of all, the Pyramid Stage where the weekend's biggest names would strut their stuff. There was a range of entertainment on offer that catered for every need, with bands and individuals performing all styles of music from classical through to rock, metal, punk and reggae. There was also the Circus Field, so named because of the big top where clowns, trapeze artists and the like would perform. There were comedy tents, a cinema field showing a wide range of movies and a field with a fairground. Other areas were known as the Green Futures Field and the Field Of Avalon and catered for those interested in worthy causes such as Greenpeace and all those other bodies dealing with the environment and similar issues. Alongside these were the Healing and Spiritual Fields for those who needed a shower, massage, haircut, shave, some physiotherapy, a dose of Hare Krishna, Christianity, Hinduism, hypnotism, spiritualism or any other ism.

The third pillar of the festival was made up of the camping

areas, with fields set aside for people to pitch their tents, and there were facilities to do so within the festival perimeter as well as on the outside. Some chose to pitch their tents on the hill that looked down on the main Pyramid Stage, thereby giving them a view of the headlining bands, while others camped in the quieter locations.

For the time being, though, all that would have to wait. Those of us on foot who'd left the van were approaching the pub just as the others were coming out through the door, having recharged their glasses, to drink their pints as they watched the traffic crawl slowly by.

'Go on then,' I prompted, looking at Gerry. 'Mine's a pint of lager.'

'What about me then?' Porky protested.

'Go on then, Gerry, get him one as well.'

Gerry smiled and did the honours, disappearing into the pub with a list of drinks. We sat at a table in the pub's front garden and enjoyed both the warm late-afternoon sun and the pleasant sur-roundings. Some three-quarters of an hour later the van pulled up alongside the pub. We finished our drinks, stepped across the low wall that divided the pub's grounds from the pavement and climbed aboard.

'Alright?' asked Billy.

'Not really,' said a hacked-off-looking Tony, who, motioning to the girls, continued, 'I've just had to sit with these four loons for the last hour. While I've been trying to keep my head together to drive the van, they've been getting pissed and stoned and giving me loads about why I didn't just pull out and overtake the cars in front of me.'

That remark brought on shrieks of laughter from the girls, and, knowing what state they could get themselves into, I felt a bit sorry for Tony. I sighed.

'How long do you think this is going to last?' I asked, motioning to the line of cars stretching into the distance in front of us.

'We're thinking about walking it and meeting you on the

inside,' said Sparky, his measured Glaswegian accent giving an air of confidence.

'What?' said a couple of the girls in unison.

'So am I,' said Tony. 'I'm fed up with driving.'

'I'm not having that,' said Lynn, suddenly switching out of her happily drunk state and giving her boyfriend Keyo a stare that could kill.

'Don't worry about it,' retorted Keyo. 'You just stay on the van. Joe will get you in, and we'll meet you on the inside – it's simple.'

'Look,' said Gerry, entering the debate, 'the less on the van, the simpler it will be to get everybody in. We'll get over the fence, sort out a spot in the kids' field and hang on until you get there.'

It made sense. The more of us on the inside, the better the chance would be that we'd be able to get the rest on the van in. After another half-hour or so in the queue, and about a mile away from the main gate, those jumping the fence left the van and disappeared into the twilight, heading towards the twelve-foot-high fence that surrounded the entire festival site. Those remaining looked at me as if to say, *What now?*

'Alright,' I said to Porky, who was driving the van, 'just follow me, do what I say and, whatever you do, don't stop for anyone unless I tell you to. Got it?'

'Go on then, Joe,' he replied. 'After you.'

It was his first visit to Glastonbury, and, despite his front, I could tell that Porky was a bit apprehensive.

'Stay cool, mate,' I said, trying to reassure him. 'Just turn right here and follow the traffic.'

As we turned on to the entrance causeway and drove slowly towards a gate that was not intended for the use of the public, a steward approached.

'Where are you going? You can't drive up here. Have you got tickets?'

'Hasn't anyone told you we're coming?' I replied. 'We're the road crew for a band from Dorset called Hoedown At Hanks. We're meant to be playing tonight, but we broke down on the way. The band managed to get a lift down here, but we had to stay with the van until we were able to hire another one. It's got all their gear in it.'

'Hoedown At Hanks?' repeated the steward.

'That's right,' I said. 'Check on your radio. We're playing tonight.'

Having been in the Dorset town of Bournemouth several weeks previously, I'd noticed a poster advertising the fact that the said band would be appearing at the festival, and their name was as good as any to throw in the hat. We were lucky. After a moment's conversation between the steward and a voice somewhere else, he broke away from his walkie-talkie.

'That's OK. Do you know where you're going?'

'We said we'd meet them near the children's field,' I replied. 'How do we get there from here?'

'I tell you what I'll do. I'll get someone to show you the way.'

He motioned to one of his fellow stewards who came over, and the situation was explained.

'No problem,' said the second steward. 'I'll get my bike and you can follow me.'

I thanked both of the security men and jumped back into the cab of the van.

'Easy,' I said. 'Just follow that guy, and we're home.'

Seconds later we had a motorcycle escort, straight through the main gate and right to where we wanted to go. Porky and the others who had been hiding in the back of the van were both amazed and in stitches laughing.

'I told you it would be sorted,' I crowed. 'Now, just keep up with the guy on the bike, and he'll take us straight to where we want to go.'

In the meantime, Tony had decided to try to get in on his own, but, after leaving the others who were set on jumping the fence, he met a first-timer to Glastonbury who wasn't quite sure which way he was meant to go and tagged along with him.

A streetwise Scouser, Tony had left the mean streets of Liverpool to look for a different life in Devon. He was another who, like the rest of us, loved bunking into places and getting something for nothing. A few years before, several of us were driving to London to watch The Rolling Stones perform at Wembley Stadium. I was in the back of the car gazing out of the window, lost in my own world. One of the others, looking at me, said, 'What's the matter, Joe? You're very quiet.' Before I could reply, Tony cut in, quick as a flash, 'He's got a ticket. It ain't the same buzz.'

It was as true then as it was with this trip to Glastonbury. The fact that we were going to the festival was great in itself, but the rush we'd get from bunking in would be the icing on the cake. However, despite the fact that Tony knew how to cheat, steal, lie and use and abuse the system to his own advantage, he always did his best to be a decent chap and be nice to everyone he met. Like the rest of us, he was a scallywag with a heart of gold.

'I'll show you the way,' said Tony to his newfound friend. 'I've been to Glastonbury a few times.'

With that, they made their way to one of the pedestrian entrances to the festival, away over on the other side from the road where Tony had left the van. As they approached Gate 2 and the marshals in charge, Tony's companion turned to him and asked, 'Have you got a ticket then or what?'

'Er, not yet, mate, but don't worry about me. I'll be alright. I'll just follow you, and if you hear me say anything just wave your ticket at the stewards, and I'll get in.'

As it happened, Tony was well and truly rumbled and was told, in no uncertain manner, 'to get away from the area as soon as he liked, if only for his own safety'. Heeding the advice, Tony turned around, went back on to the perimeter path and decided to take a right-hand turn. Within about twenty-five minutes he was nearing Gate 3.

It was then that four young guys – students probably – approached him, one of them asking him whether he'd be able to help them get in.

'I'll give it a go. I want in myself,' he said.

Tony was now walking alongside the four and, although not particularly wanting the hassle of having the extra bodies to look after, to him at least they looked likely to be of some sort of assistance as far as getting in was concerned. They continued to walk along the path that followed the perimeter fence.

'You want to get in cheap?' said a voice.

They stopped and turned. A young Hell's Angel approached.

'It'll cost you a ten-spot each. You interested?'

The four students and Tony looked at each other and, without saying anything, nodded in agreement. The greaser turned towards the hedge on the other side of the path and whistled. Through a gap in the shrubbery, a massive biker appeared.

'I've got a way in past the first line of security, and I can take you as far as the inner fence, £10 a go. You having it?'

Again the five without a ticket looked at each other and nodded. After taking a £10 note from each of the four students, he approached Tony.

'Where's your money?' he demanded.

'Fuck off, mate,' Tony replied in a deep Scouse accent. 'You've already had forty quid off of us, that'll do ya.'

The four who'd paid looked dumbstruck at his cheek, but, fearing that their money might be wasted if they pointed out the misdemeanour, they swallowed hard and bit their lips. It was a good job that the biker had been standing in front of them facing Tony when their jaws dropped, otherwise the young scally from Liverpool might have been ejected for a second time in less than half an hour. Momentarily phased by the sharp reply, the ticket man did his sums, breathed deeply and led the five through a gate and left them in front of a twelve-foot-high corrugated-iron fence that would then have to be negotiated.

'I'll never get over that,' exclaimed Tony.

''Ere you go,' said the biker. 'I'll give you a lift up.'

With that, the biker leaned against the fence, cupped his hands and gave Tony a leg-up until he reached the top of the barrier from where the grinning Scouser more or less tumbled over and on to the other side. Recovering quickly, he sat on his haunches and surveyed the scene. With the fence he'd just climbed at his back, there was, about ten yards in front of him, another barrier equally as high as the one he'd just got over. He was nearly safe with just this inner fence left to negotiate. As he stood, he could hear raised voices from where he'd just come from.

'There they are. There are four of them.'

Tony realised that the others he'd been with moments before had not been as fortunate as him and were now involved in a game of chase with the official stewards who were pursuing them. After climbing over the inner fence by way of a scaffold pole that was supporting the structure, he was in.

'Fuckin' marvellous,' he said to himself as he walked away from his point of entry and into the festival. 'If you're not fast, you're last.'

Within five minutes he'd met up with Gerry, Keyo, Billy and the others, who'd also managed to work their way in, and together they made the short journey to the prearranged meeting point. Moments later they were joined by Alan O. This, after he'd driven through an entry gate at high speed on his 1,000cc Honda, leaving the stewards no chance of stopping him and covered in the dust that his bike had kicked up. While Tony's lot had been getting themselves in, Porky, the girls and I were still on the van, and, after driving through the crowds that were already enjoying the festival, we arrived at the children's field. As the van stopped, Gerry, Keyo and the others came running up.

'See,' said Gerry, 'I told you they'd be here.'

Porky and the others were amazed. We'd just turned up. I'd done a bit of blagging, and we were in – no problem – and everybody had met up as we said we would. In truth, I'd amazed myself with the good fortune we'd had, but I didn't let anyone know that. As it stood, my reputation had been enhanced, and, following that, in subsequent years people always looked to me to get them in. No one ever got let down.

CHAPTER THREE

After the experiences of going to Glastonbury Festival in those previous years, it was an event I really looked forward to, just like a child looks forward to Christmas. Even on the journey home after a weekend at Glastonbury had come to an end, I would be thinking about the next one. And so it was in 1993.

Buzzing at the prospect of going to the festival, Billy and I had made the journey to Dorset on the preceding Tuesday to link up with a few friends of ours who lived there and travel to Glastonbury with them. Gruff, his wife H, Joanna and Samantha had borrowed a Transit van and offered to give us both a lift to the festival. As well as having tickets, on board the van they had enough home comforts to last a month, let alone the six nights and seven days we were planning on staying. Although the festival didn't officially start until Friday, people arriving early – even by a couple of days – were allowed in, and we were happy going there for the extra two days even though there wouldn't be that much in the way of bands playing. We left the Dorset seaside town at lunchtime, and, by about 2.30pm the same afternoon, we had arrived in the vicinity of the festival.

Although they had been to Glastonbury loads of times, our friends weren't really the type who took drugs and could, by some standards, be considered straight. They didn't have a problem with Billy or myself having a puff, but when it came to getting past the police, who were doing their duty and performing random stops, we were on our own.

As we approached the turn-off leading to the camping and parking fields, we could see the police directing traffic and generally putting the wind up those who were carrying illegal substances.

'This is where you get off,' said Gruff, whose wife was driving the van.

'No problem,' I said, as I stashed my own and Billy's hash down the front of my jeans. 'I'll see you in there.'

The van had stopped some three hundred yards from an officer assigned to traffic duty, and I got out. Although I was a bit brassed off at having to walk the last part of the journey, I couldn't blame Gruff for his decision. If the van was stopped and searched and our stash found – Billy and myself had taken an ounce of hash each – it might have meant everybody on board making a detour via the local police station, and there was the chance the police would have dismantled the van in an effort to find more drugs. As it was, I casually passed the officers, who didn't even give me a second glance. I now faced a walk of at least three-quarters of an hour down a country lane before I'd even reach the perimeter of the festival, and that was something I didn't fancy. As I contemplated the trek, a camper van drove slowly past.

'Any chance of a lift?' I shouted, as I caught the eye of the girl who was driving. Before she could answer, I continued, 'I don't need to get inside. I can hang on to the back.'

She laughed, looked at her travelling companions and nodded her assent. The van stopped, and I stepped on to the rear bumper and held the back-door handle. Banging the door, I gave the signal that I was on board, and the van moved off. The people in the car behind started laughing at my cheek and were good enough to hang back just in case the unthinkable happened and I lost my footing and fell on to the road. I didn't, and I arrived in the same field as Gruff, Billy and the rest of them some five minutes after they themselves had parked up.

Within an hour or so our encampment had been erected. This time, and following the lessons we had learned throughout the previous years, we'd opted to stay on the outside of the perimeter fence in one of the many camping areas. The reasons for this were simple. Because of its location, the field was situated a good six or seven minutes' brisk walk away from Gate 3, which was our nearest point of access to the main festival area. This meant that, even though the constant drone of the festival was always audible in the background, our particular spot was relatively quiet. Occasionally the sound of the performers in the Acoustic Tent might drift over if the wind was blowing in the right direction, but, on the whole, it meant relative tranquillity for us compared with those who'd chosen to camp on the inside, near one of the main stages or a place where someone had decided to set up a rave.

In addition, we'd all agreed that, security-wise, we would be better on the out than on the in. Because we were slightly off the beaten track, our area was not as densely populated as some, and we soon got to know our neighbours. They were there to enjoy the festival, see a few bands and generally chill out. Like us, they, together with 99 per cent of the Glastonbury population, would have concerns about losing their kit, as theft and robbery were, in those days and in the main, accepted as being a hazard of attending the festival. We, like the majority of all those camping that weekend, would make a reciprocal agreement with our immediate neighbours to keep our eyes open and look out for each other's stuff.

The practice generally worked well in the camping fields. Although the occasional theft did take place, occurrences were minor compared with what was happening within the festival boundaries. Over the years, the cases of people erecting their tents and going off to see a band and returning to find that not only their possessions but also the tent itself had been stolen probably number in the thousands. We'd chosen to park up next to one of the hedgerows and were out of the way in one of the furthest reaches of our field. Not many robbers would bother coming up there.

Apart from anything else, where we were was a good spot, fairly close to a water standpipe and not too badly served by a few half-decent independent traders who'd earn themselves a nice few quid selling a variety of goods ranging from ice-cream and sweets through to lager and beer.

'Right. You ready?' asked Billy.

'Yeah. Just coming.'

'Hurry up.'

'Skin a couple up for the walk.'

As I threw Billy a bit of my hash, I knew that I'd not only distracted him from his train of thought but also bought myself another couple of minutes to get myself ready for our first venture out. I double-checked my pockets to make sure I had everything I needed. Ticket, money – about £40 – puff, cigarettes, skins, Zippo lighter, chewing gum, mints together with a small plastic bag containing a toothbrush and toothpaste and a flat-pack of Wet Ones. Although some might think it a little extreme, that particular list of items has served me very well during my time attending festivals, and I'm sure many others who'd been before also carried similar hand baggage. As well as the above, I had another £50 and a couple of eighths of hash concealed within a money-belt that I was wearing beneath my jeans.

By the time I was happy with what I was carrying and picked up my lightweight windcheater, Billy had finished rolling the spliffs. We said our cheerios to those we'd travelled with and set out along the avenue of lorries, vans, trailers and tents to the gap in the hedge at the other end of the field. There, we turned left and found ourselves walking along a track that separated the fields and led towards the festival area.

As we got closer to the entry gate, we could see in the distance the far perimeter of one side of the festival. On the horizon, the trees and natural foliage of the woods that surrounded the fields was separated from the grassland by a concrete fence. Within the enclosure there was a mass of tents and huge marquees that housed several of the stages, their array of colours seemingly merging into what looked like a huge patchwork quilt, and this vividly contrasted with the natural hues of the countryside.

As we continued along the path and neared our point of entry, the human traffic got busier. The paths which led from another couple of fields in which people were camping had merged with the one that we were on, and we were joined by what seemed like hundreds of others making their way into the festival. Meanwhile, there were almost as many people coming towards us from the direction in which we were heading. Those who'd had a few hours inside the festival area were seemingly retreating to their camps for some respite.

By now, the traders selling beer, lager and spirits, as well as skins and cigarettes, had taken all the space alongside the track. There were a couple of cafés that had been set up by the traders who owned burger vans with several using camping tables and chairs to offer people a place to sit and have a tea or a coffee along with the usual selection of burgers, hotdogs and similar offerings.

Some of the fields that contain and surround the festival area are located on hills, and we had camped in one that, compared with the rest, was considerably higher. As we continued along the track, we were walking across the area known locally as Ridgy Ground. It started to lead us down a hill towards an opening. As we descended there was a noticeable rise in both the tension in the air and the amount of shady-looking characters just hanging around.

'Oi, bruv! You alright? You want something?' a black face whispered as we walked past.

As we continued to walk on, and without even looking back at him, Billy simply said, 'Nah, mate, we're sorted.'

'Got some Es if you're dancing, bruv . . .'

His words fell upon deaf ears, as both Billy and myself were focused on our point of entry to the festival proper. As we cut through the opening at the bottom of the hill, we came across a junction of a lane that led along the outside of the concrete fence we'd seen in the distance. This surrounded the whole of the inner festival area, and the section we'd camped near had a single-track road running around its perimeter. On one side there were hedges that served as boundaries for some of the camping fields that were full of tents, vans and the like, while on the other side of the road was the remainder of what used to be a tree-and-bush-lined row originally intended as a division between the road and the immediate proximity of the fence itself. However, due to the thousands of people that had, over the years, cut their way through the foliage to get up to the fence, the trees and bushes had been reduced to little or nothing in some places, while in others it was still quite thick. Across a track that was roughly fifteen feet wide, the concrete fence was clearly visible. It stood about twelve feet high and was made up of long concrete segments that were about a foot deep and ran horizontally. It was reminiscent of a section of the Berlin Wall or a prisoner-of-war camp. Every so often, a Land Rover full of stewards drove along the track hoping to deter people intent on either climbing the wall by use of a rope and grappling hook or a ladder as well as those who would try to tunnel their way through the rock and earth.

The area in front of what turned out to be the way to the gate was a hive of activity. Along with the people entering and leaving the festival were those who were waiting to meet friends. Some were sitting on their rucksacks and tents looking longingly towards the entrance and enviously at those who were coming and going. These people obviously didn't have tickets and didn't have enough money to buy one from a tout. There were also groups of people who were offering a range of services from drugs to cheap, but dodgy, admission. A rough-looking kid aged about nineteen approached.

'Have you got tickets? I can get you in for £35 each. I know where there's a hole in the fence up the path . . .'

As we already had tickets, we declined the offer and carried on walking.

'I'll get you both in for £60,' he came back.

'Cheers, mate, but we're sorted,' said Billy.

Billy and I smiled at each other and headed towards the opening in the perimeter fence. As I put my hand inside my pocket to get my ticket, we were both thinking that we should sell our tickets – we'd seen people offering to pay a few bob over face value for them – and bunk in for nothing. We stopped for a second and looked at each other.

'Can't be bothered.'

'I can't either,' said Billy.

We walked on. As we passed through the entrance, we could see both sides of the fence. Stewards who were marshalling the crowds towards either the entrance or the exit also had the task of guarding the breaks in the fence. As well as the perimeter track that ran around the outside, there was another that ran the length of the inside. That was bordered by another fence, and the gap between the two barriers served as a no-man's land. As I looked to my right, I could see a tractor pulling a trailer that was carrying about a dozen heavy-looking stewards, and this was followed by a Land Rover. The convoy headed for the inner path, and, as the fence curved away to the left in the distance, the vehicles disappeared around the corner as the stewards continued their patrol.

We then came across the entrance proper. Another two sections of concrete fencing running at near right-angles to the perimeter fence narrowed to a point where the distance between each side was wide enough to house eight turnstiles, each manned by at least three stewards. Access to these was provided by way of metal safety barriers that had been placed in rows to ensure that those entering would form orderly queues while they waited their turn to pass through. This was one of six gates located at various points along the perimeter fence, numbered from one to six funnily enough, through which all those who'd purchased a ticket would enter. Yet again, and now considering it our own spot, we entered another Glastonbury Festival through Gate 3.

To the right of the entry turnstiles was one especially set aside for new arrivals. Billy and I took our turn and waited to produce our tickets. As I handed mine over, I expected to be given a plastic band that would be placed around my wrist by a steward who would then tighten it and fasten it by way of a metal clasp which, in theory, would make sure that it could not be taken off and given to someone else. This system had been employed in previous years to allow people who wished to leave the festival to do so and, by showing the band to the stewards, would also allow them to re-enter. However, instead of giving me a wristband, the girl I'd given my ticket to simply pointed in the direction of the festival.

'Don't I get a wristband?' I asked.

'No, we're not using that system this year,' she answered.

'How do we get a pass-out then?' interjected Billy.

'You get an ultraviolet stamp on your arm when you want to leave,' she replied, 'and when you want to get back in, you put your arm under one of the lights, and the stewards will be able see the mark and let you in.'

This was totally new. In previous years the wristband had been the only proof of entry that was used. The problem for the Glastonbury officials, however, was quite simple. Once people had got past the gate, it wasn't too difficult to stretch the plastic band over the hand and remove it. That meant they were able to take them off and give them to their friends who would then leave the festival, go out to meet others and give them the bands. Once the plastic had been forced across narrowed hands and on to the wrist, they would then walk through the gates as if they'd already been in, had left and were just returning.

Some went around the festival collecting the wristbands from people who'd decided to camp within the perimeter and had no need to go out. Their bands would be exchanged for a small amount of cash or drugs and then later transferred to those waiting outside who were either friends or customers willing to pay for the privilege of borrowing a band. A regular cottage industry had developed over the years involving this particular scam, which was why the organisers of the 1993 Glastonbury Festival had decided to change the system.

The ultraviolet stamp the steward had told us about fascinated me. As soon as we had entered, Billy and I turned around and headed towards the exit turnstile. We just had to see how this new-fangled system would work. As we left through the exit gate, we were asked to hold out our arms in front of a steward. The girl then pushed a rubber stamp into a tin containing a pad of ultra-violet ink and then pressed the stamp to my arm.

'I can't see anything,' I said.

'Don't worry,' said the girl, 'it's invisible. When you come back in, just hold your arm underneath the light, and the person on the gate will be able to see the stamp.'

Still intrigued by the new arrangement, both Billy and I walked through the exit turnstiles and turned immediately to walk back through the entry gate. As we walked through the metal barriers, two girls, both of them wearing high-visibility steward's jackets, stopped us.

'Tickets? Stamps?' said one cheerfully.

'I've just been out, and I'm coming back in,' said Billy.

'You must have a stamp then. Which arm was it on?'

Billy offered his right forearm, and the girl, taking Billy's wrist, pulled it under a black-plastic bin-liner that was attached to a metal post.

'What ya doin'?' demanded Billy.

'I'm checking that you've got a stamp,' said the girl.

As Billy's arm was put under the bin-liner, the other steward peered underneath and turned on an ultraviolet light, shining it over Billy's forearm.

'Can I see?' I asked. 'I've never seen anything like that before.'

'Here, have a look,' said the first steward.

As I bent forward to see what her friend was looking at, I saw a purple mark on Billy's arm that was made visible by the ultraviolet light the steward was using to scan his limb.

'There,' she said, 'can you see that?'

As I looked, there in the purple hue was the impression from the stamp he'd received only minutes earlier. In theory, the ultraviolet light was meant to show up the 'invisible' security ink, and, on the main vein on Billy's wrist, I could just make out a small circle within which appeared the yin-yang symbol. Because of the bright afternoon sun, however, the ultraviolet light wasn't working as well as it would do when the evening came.

'I can hardly see anything,' said a slightly agitated Billy.

'Don't worry,' said the female, 'we can see it. It does work better after dark, but I promise you, you will get back in.'

'That's clever,' I said, 'but how long does it last? It won't fade away before I want to go out and come back again, will it?'

'You can get a stamp every time you leave. A few people have got them all over their arms – as long as we can see something of it, you'll be OK to get back in.'

'What happens when I have a wash?' asked Billy.

One of the girls laughed. 'Just make sure you leave a little bit of yourself that you don't wash. Seriously, though, you can have as many stamps as you like, and the ink should last two or three days anyway, so as long as you keep having a top-up you'll be fine.'

That was that. Billy and I looked at each other, thanked the girls and continued on our way through the entrance barriers. This time, though, when we came to the end of them, we continued in the direction of the festival.

Even though it was only Tuesday, it seemed as though there were thousands of people there already, and the traders were doing a brisk trade catering for those who were hungry or thirsty. It was a strange feeling walking around the festival site some three days before it was officially meant to start. Drags that would, once it had begun, be packed with people, were still easy to negotiate, as the main body of attendees would not start to arrive until the Thursday evening, with Friday being the day that the place would get really crowded. Even so, and at this early stage, the prospect of the buzz and adrenalin from the weekend to come was already permeating the atmosphere.

We stopped for a bite to eat. I paid the bill, and, after buying a couple of cans of Coke to wash our food down, I was gutted to find that I'd spent more than a tenner.

'It's only Tuesday, and I'm on the way to being skint already. I'm devastated.'

'Skin up then,' said Billy. 'We'll still have a ball.'

'How much money have you got then?' I enquired.

'About £50 – it's all I had left out of my giro.'

I sighed. 'I've got about that as well, and we've got three days before it starts properly, so we'd better watch what we're doing money-wise.'

'Stop moaning and skin up.'

We walked on down Stage Road, the main drag towards the Pyramid Stage, the slight wind blowing up dust from the track as the sun shone down. It reminded me of a one-horse town from an old Western film, and I expected to see a loose bit of brush blow by at any moment.

It was different when it was less crowded. One could walk anywhere with ease and peruse all that was on offer at the various stalls without getting caught up in the crowds that would subsequently arrive. It was great getting there early, even though the main event didn't start until Friday. There would still be loads to do and see come Thursday, with plenty of unsigned bands performing at various points throughout the festival site and, of course, the dance parties that would send pulsing drumbeats across the festival area and far into the surrounding countryside.

'Hey, Joe.'

I looked around. There was Barry, a friend of the people Billy and I had travelled with, and someone I'd met the previous year. He walked across the dirt track and shook both of us by the hand.

'How ya doin'?' I asked.

'Yeah, I'm OK. Did you bunk in, or did you buy a ticket?' said Barry.

'We bought tickets this time,' said Billy.

'What about this ultraviolet stamp then?' he asked. 'That's going stop a lot of people getting in.'

'I know,' I said. 'It's not going to be as easy getting people in this year.'

'I was told that they were going to use the stamps this year – I brought a couple of ultraviolet security marker pens with me just in case I couldn't get in, but, as it happens, I managed to jump the fence. I don't suppose you want them, do you?'

Billy and I looked at each other.

'Yeah, we'll have them,' I replied, as Barry searched his ruck-sack before finding the pens and handing them over.

'Do you think you'll be able to do anything with them then?' Barry asked.

'Yeah, we'll give it a go,' said Billy. 'We'll see you later and let you know how we get on.'

'We're staying up by Gate 3 near where we were last year, so come up and find us later, and we'll have a smoke and a few drinks,' I added.

We shook hands, and Barry turned to walk in the opposite direction to us.

'See you later,' he said as he waved his goodbyes. We never saw him again.

I turned to Billy.

'Let's head for home and have a little chat . . .'

'Good idea, Joe, let's go,' he replied.

We made our way back to base, but when we went through the exit we made sure the stewards marked our forearms with fresh ultraviolet stamps and ensured that, when we asked if we could see them under the light, we got a good look at them. My original stamp had been covered with half of the new one, leaving my arm looking like it had a figure eight on it.

'Is that alright?' I asked.

'Yes,' said a steward reassuringly, 'as long as we can see something of the stamp, you'll be OK. If you like, I can give you a few more.'

Billy and I looked at each other and grinned.

'Go on then, darling,' said Billy to the girl who was in charge of the stamp, as if emphasising the charming side of his Glaswegian nature.

With his hand held firmly by the steward, his arm was then stamped another seven or eight times. Once his other arm had been covered, it was my turn. We checked ourselves under the stewards' ultraviolet light, and they were by now just a blur of yellowy shapes with no discernible pattern, although at the edge there were some clearly defined circles.

'Sure that's going to be alright? Billy asked. 'It won't come off when I wash, will it?'

'You'll be OK,' replied the girl.

I smiled at Billy.

'You'll be alright – your daddy's here.'

As we made our way up the lanes, we again passed all the

people hanging around, obviously ticketless and waiting in the hope that they'd somehow get in. Billy and I didn't say a word to each other as we walked by them, but, as we made our way up the incline towards our camp, the pace we were setting was nearly as fast as the thoughts of fortunes to be made racing through our minds.

CHAPTER FOUR

None of the people we had travelled with was at the camp, and it seemed everyone else in our field had also left their tents and gone into the festival, leaving myself and Billy on our own to discuss how exactly we would take advantage of the ultraviolet pens we'd been given.

'Where d'ya think you haven't got a stamp then?'

Billy looked back at me as if I was an idiot.

'I don't fuckin' know!' he shouted back, even though I was no more than two feet away from him.

I tried again.

'Where do you *think* you haven't got a stamp?'

He looked at me again, shook his head and started laughing.

'It's invisible . . . and I cannae remember.'

'Look! It's quite simple. Give us your arm and I'll try drawing one on. It's got to be in a place where there aren't any already so that we know it works.'

'What if it doesn't?'

'It don't matter if it doesn't work. Bang goes any money, but we'll still get in. Anyway, it is going to work.'

'Why don't you try it then?'

'We'll both do it. Now, draw a line around this 10p bit and then fill half of the circle in.'

I held out my forearm and pointed to a spot I was sure hadn't been stamped before, and, taking one of the ultraviolet markers, Billy did the honours. Once he'd finished, I rubbed over the circle with the inside of my wrist.

'What d'ya do that for?'

''Cos you ain't done a yin-yang sign, have ya?'

He looked at me with a half-blank, half-pissed-off expression. Being an 'off-the-street' Glaswegian, the chances were that Billy had never heard of the expression, let alone knew anything about the ancient Chinese philosophy.

'It won't matter,' I continued. 'All you've got to say is that you've been out and had a wash, and it must have got smudged when you were rubbing your arms or drying them.'

'Here . . .'

Billy handed me the marker, and I drew a stamp on his arm, and again I rubbed over the spot with my wrist. Billy just gave me one of his looks.

'Come on,' I said quietly, 'let's give it a go.'

We left everything of value back at the camp, including our spending money, which we each hid in our own dirty-washing bags, and walked down to the entry gate with just enough puff to keep us going for a few hours, the ultraviolet pens and a 10p coin each. There were loads of people hanging about, and, if it did work, we might end up doing well. First, though, we'd have to test it and put the marks we'd made ourselves under the scrutiny of the stewards who were checking the stamps of those re-entering the festival.

Within a few minutes we were approaching Gate 3 and joined the queues of people waiting for their stamps to be checked. When our turn came, we held out our arms, and, after a cursory glance, the stewards let us both in. As soon as we'd gone through the entry gate we turned and walked up through the exit aisle. As Billy drew alongside me, we looked at each other but said nothing.

We were back on the lane within about two minutes, and we started walking up towards where we'd camped. Two guys and two girls were coming towards us, and, judging by the amount of kit they were carrying, it was clear that they'd just arrived.

'Have you got tickets?' I whispered just as they passed.

They stopped. One of the guys, laughing, turned.

'I suppose you've got a hole under the fence or a ladder. Which one is it?'

'I'm not getting over that fence,' said one of the girls, a horrified expression crossing her face as she looked at the obstacle.

'Nah, better than that,' I replied. 'You know it's not wristbands this year, don't you?'

'I've heard,' said the guy, 'they've got some kind of new security arrangement. Something to do with an ink stamp or something.'

'It's not quite like that . . .' I came back at him and then explained how the system worked.

'And how much do you want for drawing a stamp on us then?'

'It should be £20 a head, but I'll do the lot of you for £60.'

He looked at his companions. With the price of a ticket that year set at £58, it was nothing less than a bargain-basement offer, all four of them in for a couple of quid over the price it would have cost one person had they used the official channels.

'How do we know it will work?' said the other guy. 'How do we know you won't rip us off?'

'Look, we're not like that . . .'

The four looked at each other and then at us.

'How about if I stamp two of you and the other two wait here. Once you've got in and seen it work, you can come out and get the other two.'

Billy cut in. 'He'll take you down, and I'll wait here with your pals. We can look after your bags and stuff so it doesn't look like you've just arrived and then, once two of you are in and stamped up, we can carry your bags in for you. If any of the stewards want to know why we've got bags, we'll just say we're moving from where we were camping to another spot. Simple.'

One of the girls, looking at me, said, 'Yeah, but you could still run off with our money.'

'I won't take any money off you until you've got in. Once

46

you're through you can pay me, and we'll do the same for your mates.'

The four of them looked at each other while Billy and I stood back to give them space and allow them to talk.

'Fifteen pounds each,' I heard one person say. 'That's not bad.'

Billy looked at me, and I held my breath. One of the guys turned and faced us.

'You'll take us through?'

'Yeah.'

'And you don't want any money from us till we get in?'

'That's right.'

'And you'll come back and get our friends?'

'Yeah. No problem.'

He turned to face his companions.

'Let's give it a try. We've got nothing to lose.'

Between us, Billy and I stamped up the four of them, and, as I smudged the ink on the arms of the pair with me, I said to each of them, 'Have a nice time,' repeating the phrase to the two with Billy. I left him with one of the couples and walked down towards the gate with the ones who were going to go through first. They'd left their bags with their friends so it didn't appear to the stewards that they'd just arrived. As we joined the queue to get in, the girl looked slightly apprehensive.

'Stay cool,' I said. 'There's no problem. Just watch me, and do what I do.'

Our turn came, and getting them in was as simple as I thought it would be. We sailed past the steward checking the stamps without him giving us a second glance. Once through and into the festival, we immediately turned to leave through the exit barriers, and I made sure that the couple with me got two or three official stamps each before we made the short journey back to where we'd left their friends.

'Did it work?' said the girl who was waiting with Billy.

'Easy,' said the guy who'd come in with me.

With that, the couple with Billy picked their bags up, ready to walk down to the gate.

'Do you want the money now?' asked one of the girls.

'You're OK. We'll get it off you once you get in. You're not thinking of doing a runner are you?' I replied, half jokingly.

'No chance,' said her boyfriend. 'You've done us a favour getting us in, and, anyway, we wouldn't do that.'

Billy came with us this time, and, as in the case of the first couple, the two who hadn't yet been through didn't carry any bags with the first pair taking their own and Billy and me doing the donkeywork on behalf of the new entrants. Again, they went through unchallenged, and it was all smiles as, once the four of them were inside, one of the guys handed over their £60.

As I took the money from him, his girlfriend said, 'We've got some friends who wanted to come, but they haven't got any tickets. If we can get to a phone and call them, do you think you'd be able to get them in?'

'No problem,' Billy said, 'but you'll have to come and find us so we can meet them. I don't know how we'll do that, though.'

'When are they due to get here?' I asked.

'I should think that if they know they can get in they'll be here tomorrow.'

'How many of them?' asked Billy.

'Six, maybe seven . . .'

Knowing the area around Gate 3 quite well, I'd already made my mind up to work the stamp there, and Billy agreed. At the entrance, it was busy with loads of people hanging around, and it was as good a place as any to call our patch.

'If they come tomorrow,' I said, 'you'll find us somewhere around where we met you. Just wait around until you see one of us, and we'll sort them out.'

With the arrangements made, they headed off into the

festival, and we returned to the lanes that we'd decided we'd work.

As we walked up, I gave Billy his £30. As he took it, he said quietly, 'This is going to be good.'

After an hour or so we had got another ten people inside, in ones and twos, at £20 per head, and we both felt like we were on a roll. We'd decided between us to halve the money as we got it, in case one or the other of us was captured, and if the worst did come to the worst we'd be able to split what the other one had left.

We had also got ourselves into a sort of rhythm, and it was working well. We'd stop and ask potential candidates if they wanted a cheap entry, and, with the knowledge that we were acquiring with every person we got in, we were prepared with all the answers they needed.

'You don't pay till you get in. If you don't get in, you don't pay,' was the one line that always seemed to sway them, and, once they'd accepted and received a stamp and the ritualistic smudge, we'd always say, 'Have a nice time.' If, once we'd given them the patter, they didn't fancy what we were offering, they could always go elsewhere and try to get in another way.

However, those who were working the tunnels under the fence and the holes through it were taking the money before the punters got in. The same applied to those who had knotted ropes and rope ladders that were attached to grappling hooks. These were thrown over the top of the barrier and pulled back until the hook caught the top of the fence. Once secured, the punters would then have to use the rope to climb to the top, jump down to the ground on the other side and rely on either their friends or those who they'd paid to help them get their bags over. The major problem with that system of entry was that, even though they might have got over or under the first fence, they were only as far as the no-man's land between that and the inner fence. This gap was regularly patrolled by stewards, and the sight of a Land Rover full of disappointed people being driven to a security gate before being ejected was common.

The people taking the money weren't bothered. As far as they were concerned, they had sold a ticket to get over the main fence and if people got caught once they'd jumped it, it wasn't their responsibility. Additionally, in a few instances people had handed over their money only to see the person they'd given it to suddenly run off, leaving them extremely pissed off.

In total contrast, the way that Billy and I were getting people in was risk free, with those we'd taken money from extremely happy with the deal we offered. The more we took through, the more our confidence grew. We started taking it in turns to walk our customers through the gate while the other one stayed on the outside, either waiting with friends of those going through or looking for more business from fresh arrivals. We made a point of being friendly, gaining the punters' trust and generally assisting them in any way we could. Ripping people off didn't come into the equation. There was no need to, and it wouldn't have been something I'd have felt comfortable doing. I just wanted a hassle-free way of making money, and I wanted the people that we took in to feel that we'd provided a service.

Over the next hour or so we got ourselves a fair bit of business, and by the time six o'clock came we decided to stop for a break and made our way back to our camp. I thought that we might have made about £250 each but wasn't exactly sure, because when we did take the money it was split, as arranged, Billy stuffing his share deep into his jeans pockets and me putting mine into my money-belt. Once we were out of the way of prying eyes within the safety of my tent, we both took out our cash and had a count-up. Having done so, we both found that we had £290 each.

'What are you going to do with yours?' asked Billy.

'I'm keeping £40 and giving the rest to H to look after.'

'Aye, I think I'll do the same.'

We left my tent and walked to the back of H and Gruff's van where, with the doors open and their legs dangling out, they were sitting down to eat. I looked at H and started smiling.

'What are you after?' she said.

'Fancy doing us a favour?'

Gruff looked at Billy and me with a part-worried, part-inquisitive expression.

'What's it involve?' he said, cutting in.

'I want you or H to look after some money for us.'

Gruff's eyes narrowed.

'What have you two been up to then?'

Gruff had always been a bit of a worrier, and the sight of Billy and myself suddenly appearing with wads of money that had seemingly appeared out of nowhere caused him some concern. However, once we explained fully what we were doing, H burst into laughter, gave her husband a pacifying look and held out her hand.

'Go on then,' she said, 'give it to me.'

We handed over our £250 bundles and a tenner for each of them by way of a thank you, leaving us with £30 each. Sitting with them for the length of time it took to build and smoke a joint, Billy and I decided to go downtown into the festival and get ourselves something to eat.

Once we had walked down the lane towards Gate 3, we realised there was too much business about to bother with something as trivial as eating and, for the next three hours, we carried on working. By 10.30pm we'd refilled our pockets with money. We'd already seen H, Gruff and their mates pass us on the lane on their way down towards the festival, so when we got back to camp to deposit our money we would have to stash it ourselves. That didn't really worry us, as the chance of someone finding where we'd hidden our cash was slight. It was dark, and all we'd have to do was wrap it in a plastic bag and put it under or near the rubbish, or under our tents. It would be safe enough.

Back in my tent, and with the light of a torch, we counted what we had taken on our second shift and were more than pleased to find we had another £210 each. Loosening a pair of rolled-up socks, I added £40 of the £50 I still had left from before we started. I folded £250 in £10 and £20 notes together, as did Billy, and the packages were duly hidden under the corner of our tent.

'Doing well, Billy,' I said. 'Five ton stashed, and I've still got money in my pocket. I'm buzzing.'

'Aye, me, too. Tell you what, though, I've got to get something to eat.'

I agreed. It had been hours since food had passed our lips, and the energy we'd used doing all the walking in and out of the gate had made me feel more than a little peckish.

'Where we going then?'

'I fancy a proper sit-down,' replied Billy. 'I'm going to have the works.'

'Yeah, me, too, but I'm going up to the Green Fields for mine.'

'I'm not bothered where we go, but I've got to eat something soon.'

'Let's go then. Shall we build a spliff to walk round with?'

Yet again, and for the umpteenth time that day, we walked down the lanes. Now, however, the mood outside the gate had changed. Whereas earlier, in the daylight, people could see what was going on, in the dark it was a different matter. Unless you were near the gate and its security floodlights, it was hard to see more than twenty yards in front of where you were going. In the shadows, the people hanging around the lane and in front of the gate looked that little bit more dodgy. It was still very busy, but we ignored anyone who tried to speak to us and just walked on and into the festival.

We went along the drag that led from the entrance to the field where the Acoustic Tent was, down to the Pyramid Stage, officially called Stage Road, and turned left at the Meeting Point and walked up the Causeway towards the Green Fields. Billy wasn't bothered what he ate, but I wanted a vegetarian meal, and where we were headed was the best place at Glastonbury to get one.

The Green Fields had an aura of calm and stillness, and the pace of life there was appreciably slower than that just a matter of several hundred yards along the route we'd just followed. There was a definite change of atmosphere the nearer one got to the Green Fields. This area was generally the preserve of what many might describe as the archetypal festival-goer, with the sight of men sporting long hair, goatee beards, beads and flared trousers and, in the warmth of the day, women wearing cheesecloth saris and sometimes no clothes at all – a scene that seemed to be in total contrast to the madness that was the main drag and the main music and dance areas.

The Green Fields didn't have stages featuring bands or any other entertainment, as was common in the other parts of the festival, but it was the area for those who practised arts and crafts such as traditional wood-turning, basket-weaving and the construction of wicker fences. It was also the place to go for anyone who sought meditation, natural and spiritual healing and holistic cures.

I pointed out a café that I fancied from one of the outlets selling food on the Causeway, while Billy went to get a meal of his choice. I joined the queue, ordered and sat on a bench outside and waited for him to return. He was back within fifteen minutes, having bought himself a giant double-quarter-pounder beefburger and a couple of chocolate milkshakes, while I sat with my vegetarian curry, a bowl of fresh fruit and cream and a couple of smoothies. We didn't talk while we ate but instead exchanged the occasional smile. Ordinarily we'd have tried to keep the spending per meal to about a fiver. With money burning a hole in our pockets, we weren't concerned about the cost of this particular scoff and relished every mouthful, only speaking once we had finished.

'Fancy doing a bit more then or what?'

'Aye,' Billy said with a nod of his head.

We walked back through the festival and went towards Gate 3. Although there were still bodies in the area, it wasn't as busy as it had been earlier, and there weren't as many shady-looking people hanging about. Nevertheless, we decided to work away from the entrance, preferring to pick up some trade from those we'd meet a bit further up the lanes. There were fewer people the further we went from the gate, and it made it easier to both sell our product and be inconspicuous at the same time.

There would be a little more walking to do, what with seeing our customers in through the gate and then returning to the out-side, but the thought of making money kept us going. If we stayed closer to the gate we would probably have made more and in a shorter time, but there would be a chance we might be sussed by either the stewards or a bunch of scallies. We both agreed we were happy working where we were.

Travelling from every corner of the UK and beyond, people got to Glastonbury at all hours, and that ensured that new arrivals came in a relatively steady stream throughout the night. By the time we decided we'd had enough, the early-morning sun was already rising and, returning to the tents and counting our money, we found that we'd both earned another £180 each. The thought of that, together with the £500 we had in the bank plus our spending money, gave us both reason enough to have sweet dreams for the next few hours.

CHAPTER FIVE

After three hours' sleep, I woke up sweating from the heat that came from the sun burning down on my tent. I unzipped the flap and opened it to let in some fresh air and poked my head outside, where I saw H and Gruff sitting on the grass chatting with their friends Sam and Joanna.

'What time is it?' I asked.

'Ten o'clock,' H said, looking at her watch.

Reaching out through the entrance, I put my hand under the corner of the shelter and retrieved the package of money that I had hidden when we returned in the early hours and added the cash that I'd taken during the night. Pulling on a pair of shorts and a T-shirt, I stepped out and walked over to where the others were sitting, and Billy, who was already awake, dressed and sitting outside his tent, followed moments later.

'Good night last night?' I asked.

'It was great. What about you? You looked busy when we passed you,' replied Gruff.

'Yeah, we done well. Fancy looking after a bit more dosh for us, H?'

She smiled and laughed, tossing her head so that her dread-locked blonde hair moved forward in front of her face and then backwards so it fell behind her shoulders. Gruff's dreads seemed to stand on end. He cocked his head and narrowed his eyes.

'You're not gonna get us in any trouble, are you?'

'We made sure no one saw us coming back here, Gruff. We don't want to get nicked ourselves, let alone fuck it up for you lot . . . Trust me.' I said as I smiled what I hoped was a reassuring smile.

'You fuckin' worry me, you do.'

He shook his head before swigging on a bottle of beer. Billy and I laughed, as did H, and we each gave her our parcels from the night before.

'How much this time?' she asked.

'Once we give you this, you'll have six and a half from us both,' said Billy. The scar that he'd worn for years on his left cheek after crossing a Glaswegian drug lord seemed to join up with his broad grin. 'Four hundred pounds each and, with what we gave you earlier, your life is now worth £1,300 of *our* money.'

Gruff choked on the mouthful he'd just started swallowing and spat it out.

'*How* much?' he said, sounding amazed.

I drew a breath.

'Six hundred and fifty pounds each, Gruff. We're doing well. No one's getting stung, and everybody loves us. It won't come on top, and we won't bring trouble up here, I promise you.'

He looked at the pair of us.

'You take care.'

'Cheers, Gruff. Cheers, H. Do you want a couple of bob for yourselves?' said Billy.

'No, we all had a nice drink on that twenty quid you gave us last night. You keep your money . . . and take care.'

'Cheers, mate,' I said and turned to acknowledge Sam and Joanna. Like Gruff and H, these two might be considered quite straight, although it wasn't to say that they didn't know what went on.

'What is it you're doing then?' asked Joanna, a round-faced girl with long, straight dark hair.

'We're getting people without tickets in,' said Billy.

'How's that work then?' asked Sam, who was a pretty girl with blonde hair, aged twenty-three, a year or so younger than Joanna.

I told them the procedure.

'How much would you charge us?' said Sam.

'How do you mean?' said Billy. 'You're already in.'

'Our boyfriends wanted to come, but they couldn't get tickets,' said Joanna. 'Could you get them in?'

'No problem,' I said.

'How much will it cost?' said Sam.

I looked at Billy.

'Nothing, eh, Billy . . .'

'Aye, no problem. We'll get them in for nothing.'

'Where's the phone box?' asked Sam.

'Away down in the festival,' replied Billy. 'When are they coming?'

'If we ring them now they'll come tonight,' said Joanna. 'I'm going to call Pete.'

'That's OK then,' I said. 'But do me a favour. I've a couple of mates from football who want to come. Their names are Ian Seymour and Jim Luck, and they'll be coming with Ian's son Adam and his nephew Simon. If I give you Ian's number, can you call him and tell him to get down here. If they can link up with your boyfriends, we'll sort them all out at the same time.'

'I'll come with you,' Sam said, looking at Joanna before picking up her pouch of tobacco, lighter and other little bits that were on the grass next to where she was sitting.

'Thanks, Billy. Thanks, Joe.'

They stood and walked over to their tent. H looked at us.

'Thanks,' she smiled.

Gruff nodded his head slightly in a somewhat begrudging acknowledgement that we'd done the girls a favour.

'Take care,' he repeated, half smiling.

We both smiled back and went to our tents.

'You coming out, Billy, or what?'

'Aye, but I want something to eat first.'

'Have something here.'

'Like what?'

'Ask Gruff and H for something. I'm going to. Do that, and we could get going straight away.'

'I'm not eating their hippy shite,' he said, a touch disdainfully. 'I fancy a nice big fry-up.'

'Well I'm having something here and going to work.'

'I'll see you when I get back. I won't be long.'

Billy left to get a breakfast, and once I had completed my ablutions, dressed and begged and eaten a bowl of H's cereal, I sat on my own by my tent and rolled a few spliffs. The first thing I had thought of when I woke that morning was how much money we'd made the previous day and how easy it was. I was buzzing with the idea of it. For me, the feel of a wad of money in my pocket was one that wasn't easily beaten, and I made up my mind that I was going to earn as much as I could.

Like Billy, I was hungry, although my appetite was not for food but £10 and £20 notes. I wanted to start straight away, but Billy would be gone for at least an hour, and, in my mind, I weighed up how hard and dangerous it would be to work the stamp myself.

Now that it was daylight again, most of the danger that accompanied the darkness had passed, and I reckoned I'd be able to keep myself out of any serious trouble either with a crew, the stewards or the police. Obviously I would make sure that the coast was clear before I approached anyone, and I'd be selective in who I asked. That said, some, who at first appear to be the nicest of people, can turn out to be the nastiest, and it might be a bit of problem collecting the money.

The day before, Billy and I had learned two main ways of getting the people in. If, for instance, there were four of them, we'd take them all through at the same time. Once they had been stamped up, they would then be escorted through the gates by Billy and me. One of us would be at the front, leading the four in, while the other would be at the back, immediately behind the last person. When one of us had got past the stewards checking the stamps, we'd stand and collect the money from each of the punters as they passed through. If any of them decided to try their luck and run, the one of us at the back could hold on to the last person until they coughed up and covered the price for those who'd left, or their friends came back and paid us what we were owed.

The other method of working was easier, but the punters were a little more suspicious. If there were six or seven awaiting entry, we'd try to persuade two or three of them to give it a go first, and one of us would take them through the gate, leaving the other with those outside. Once those who'd tested the system had been through and returned to collect their friends, we hoped that just stamping the remainder would suffice and they'd be happy to pay on the spot, as that saved us the bother of walking them through ourselves.

I rolled a joint and thought about it some more – £650 for a night's work, and the bug had bitten me. I wanted more and decided to go and try it alone. If it didn't happen, or I didn't fancy it, I could always go inside and have a look around and maybe catch up with Billy. I checked how much money I had on me and counted £35. That would be enough. Checking my jeans pocket to make sure I had my pen and everything else I needed for a spell away from the camp, I set out for the lanes.

I got as far as the gate of our field when I saw three people sitting on the verge on the other side of the lane. They had rucksacks and bags with them and looked like they hadn't been in. Judging by their demeanour, I reckoned they were looking towards the festival reflectively and in a way that told me that they didn't have tickets.

'Hiya.'

The two girls and the guy looked up but said nothing.

I tried again. 'Have you been in yet?'

'Not yet. We haven't got any tickets,' said one of the girls.

'I can get you in.'

She smiled.

'Oh yeah?'

I explained how it worked.

'How much?' said the guy.

'It should be £20 per person, but I'll do you a special and take the lot of you for £50. How's that sound?'

The three of them agreed and offered me the money on the spot. I refused it, preferring to take the cash from them once they were in. At least I'd seen that they had the money and one of the girls nominated herself to hold it and hand it over. I stamped them up, smudged the marks on their arms and wished them the best of times. They'd all been to Glastonbury before, each without a ticket, but the previous year one of the girls had twisted her ankle when she jumped over the fence, and she didn't fancy trying it again. While we chatted on our way down the lane, my mind was elsewhere.

This was easy. Even if Billy didn't want to work, I'd do it myself. OK, so I'd lost a tenner, but it was still £50, and I was happy with that. It would be worth my while to offer a discount on the original £20 almost straight away, depending on which way I thought negotiations were going. After all, £15 per head was better than nothing. I had money saved, money to spend in my pocket and another £50 that I'd just earned. If I could keep this up until I had £1,000, I'd be more than happy.

We approached the gate. I went through first, showing the three new entrants what to do and, as in the case of everyone else, they breezed past the stewards manning the turnstiles. Once inside, the money was handed over without question and another three people were more than happy with the way things had turned out. Wishing them all the best for a great weekend again, I turned and made my way back through the exit and up to the lane.

Over the course of the next hour or so, I took in another nine people at £15 each, picking them up away from the entrance and out of sight of the scallies who, as the morning wore on, were beginning to congregate near Gate 3. Having now walked in and out of the gate five times already, I was aware that some were beginning to take notice of me. If I was making some of them, it was obvious that some of them would be wondering what I was up to. With such thoughts in my head, it was now that I wished that Billy was with me. If it did go off, I'd rather have somebody else there on my side to help me rather than have to fight my way out of trouble alone.

As I was weighing up the pros and cons, I put my hands inside my jeans pockets and felt the money-belt that was hidden underneath. I'd earned another £185 that morning and was getting close to my £1,000 target. Another few hours, and I'd be there. As I took a conscious decision to carry on whether Billy was with me or not, my heart seemed to miss a beat, and I got a feeling that, although things might get a little bit hairy, I would be OK. Anyway, I reasoned with myself, it had been a long time since I'd made money this easily, and I didn't want the chance to clean up pass me by. Just as I sat down by the side of the lane, Billy appeared.

'How ya doin'?' he asked.

'OK,' I replied, 'I'm doing alright. There's been plenty of business, and I reckon there will plenty more to come.'

'Did you make much money then?' Billy asked, half inquiringly, half begging.

I put my hand down the front of my jeans and into my money-belt. I pulled out £50 in £10 notes and handed them to Billy.

'There you go,' I said, 'and don't say I don't look after you.'

'Cheers, pal,' he responded, before adding, 'Fancy doing a bit?'

'Go on then, but not for long – I want to go down and get something to eat myself.'

We carried on for another couple of hours, earning £200 between us. I was glad to have got back the £50 that I'd given Billy and pleased to have earned another £50 towards my target. Now, as it stood, I was just over £100 away from it. However, the concerns I'd had about being spotted were also expressed by Billy, and we decided to go back to our camp and drop the money off. Once we'd taken a stroll through the festival, and I'd had something to eat, we'd then go around to one of the other gates to do a bit there. Not only would our faces not be known by the stewards and those hanging about but the change of scenery would probably do us good.

Again we made our way back up the lane, and, after we'd stashed most of the money we'd made under Gruff's van, we turned to make our way out of our field and towards Gate 2, a walk of at least twenty minutes. Just then, a guy who was camping next to us rode across the grass on his motorbike, heading for his tent. As he slowed to a halt and dismounted, I caught his eye.

'Alright, mate, how ya doing?'

'Yeah, OK, how about yourselves?'

'Yeah, we're doing OK,' I replied. 'Fancy earning yourself a couple of bob?'

Billy looked at me quizzically, as did the biker.

'Doing what?' he asked.

'By giving me and my mate a lift round to Gate 2. It'll be worth a fiver . . .'

The rider smiled.

'No problem. One at a time, or can you both get on?'

'We'll both get on, if it's all the same to you.'

'Nice one,' said Billy as I jumped on behind the rider, handed him a £5 note and shifted up as close as I could to him so that Billy would have enough room on the seat behind me. We set off three-up, and within what seemed like a couple of minutes we'd driven along Cockmill Lane, the road that ran around the perimeter fence, and arrived at our destination. We dismounted, and both Billy and I thanked the biker for the lift. As he rode off, he turned to look at us, put his thumb up and called back, 'Anytime, lads.'

'Cheers, mate,' I called back before turning to Billy. 'That's OK, ain't it? We've got our own personal taxi service now, and it's right next to where we live – we're laughing.'

Billy chuckled. 'This is the life.'

CHAPTER SIX

By the time Wednesday night had turned into the early hours of Thursday morning, me and Billy had taken another thirty or so people in, making ourselves a further £280 each. I was more than pleased, as it meant the £1,000 figure I'd hoped for had been achieved. I now had £1,100 stashed and about £80 in my pocket to see me through the rest of the night and the following day. While Billy decided to get a few hours' sleep, I wandered down to the festival and took a walk up towards the Green Fields. It was a chilled-out place, and the people who frequented the cafés and 'crash-out' tents were generally more laid back than those who didn't seem to appreciate what might be described as the hippy culture. Those who spent most of their time at Glastonbury within this area were, more often than not, the types who lived the life 365 days a year and not just for a few days during the summer at a festival in Somerset.

They referred to the Stage Road area of Glastonbury as Babylon and the people who came to watch the bands as day-trippers. I liked it in the Green Fields, and being in and around that area was, for me at least, always a pleasing experience. After the hours I'd spent traipsing back and forth through the gates, I was especially glad to reach this part of the festival site and grab the chance to get something to eat, smoke a few joints and rest my legs, which by now had become heavy and tired from all the walking involved in working the stamp.

Most years I'd have probably stayed in and around the Green Fields until just before dawn. Then, as the daylight was beginning to permeate the black of night, I'd have gone to the Stones, a circle of large boulders situated at one of the furthest points within the festival perimeter. This night, though, I was happy to crash in one of the field's large marquees and drift off into a well-earned couple of hours' sleep.

I woke at about 4am, feeling refreshed and ready for another day's work. I rolled a joint and surveyed the scene. By the light of the gas lamps that lit one corner of the marquee, I could see that the shelter in which I'd fallen asleep was full almost to bursting point with prostrate bodies, some covered, some not, but all of them either dozing or sound asleep. Some were fortunate enough to have sleeping bags to aid their slumber, and there were a few couples who were cuddling for warmth, while others, not as lucky and without a partner or something to cover themselves with, looked like they were half frozen. Although the Glastonbury Festival was held in late June, when it could be exceedingly warm during the day, the nights could be extremely cold. Unless one had a sleeping bag, a blanket or a warm coat to cover up with, the hours between sunset and sunrise could be very uncomfortable.

Having had a few years' experience of going to festivals, I was well prepared for almost any eventuality and had, the last time I'd been at our camp, taken the precaution of putting on a heavy jumper and an old working jacket, and with those two items of clothing I'd managed to keep myself snug and warm throughout the night. Looking around at those asleep, it wasn't hard to spot the people who'd found it hard work dropping off, as they were the ones with strained expressions on their faces and who were curled up in a ball and shivering as they slept. As I smoked my joint, I couldn't help chuckling out loud when I looked at those who were freezing cold. Although I found their plight amusing, my conscience was eased by the fact that I felt a little sorry for them and reasoned that they would survive, live to tell the tale and learn an invaluable lesson from their shortsightedness.

Having finished my spliff, I yawned, stretched and stood up, began to make my way out of the shelter of the marquee on to

Clapps Lane, the drag that would lead down to the Causeway and then on to Babylon. As I left the field and turned to make my way down the hill, a van drove by heading in the direction in which I wanted to go. As it passed, I ran along behind it, stepped up on to the footplate below the rear licence plate and, with my fingers, gripped the ridge that ran across the top of the back doors. The people in the cab didn't seem to notice me or, if they did, they weren't bothered, and within a couple of minutes I found myself at the Meeting Point at the junction of the Causeway and Stage Road and the right-hand turn towards the field housing the Acoustic Tent. Just as the van turned to the left to continue its journey along the drag towards the Pyramid Stage, I jumped off. The lift I'd hitched had shaved ten minutes off the walk I'd have had to make, and any saving of such a kind was, in my book at least, a bonus. From there, I made my way towards Gate 3, and, after ten minutes' walk, I was back at our camp.

Billy was still asleep as I opened the flap of his tent, and, judging by the sound of the snoring that was coming from Gruff's van, so was everybody else. Taking my wash bag out of my tent, I began the procedure of cleaning myself up. Because everybody else was sleeping, I had no qualms about going through the motions in what, by now, was broad daylight, something I would usually have performed within the privacy of my own tent.

Going to the toilet at Glastonbury was, for many, a terrible trial. They were horrible places to have to visit, and tales of what they were like was enough to put many people off going to the festival altogether. I'd never used them except on the odd occasion when it was too crowded to urinate outdoors. I definitely would never have used them to have a crap. I had my own method.

Laying out an old newspaper on the ground, I simply squatted above it and let nature take its course. Once I'd finished and had wiped myself clean, I then got the washing-up bowl that I brought with me and poured in some of the water from the container that those in our camp were sharing. Using the water and soap which I had brought with me, I gave myself a serious scrub in the nether regions – both front and back – and felt both clean and refreshed. Once dry, I put on a clean pair of boxer shorts, replaced my jeans and was ready to wash the rest of my body.

Refilling the bowl with clean water and starting from my head, I washed down to my feet having, in effect, a stand-up bath. It never failed to surprise or shock me when I saw the state some people allowed themselves to get into. The weather could be very hot, causing people to sweat excessively or, sometimes, when it was very wet, the festival became extremely muddy, and the dirt and the mud got everywhere. Keeping clean was, for me at least, one of the most important tasks when attending a festival.

The first festival I'd ever been to was at Stonehenge, and there the crew I was with were some forty or so miles away from where they lived, and at least one of them was going back home and returning to the festival site every day. Being a free festival with no restrictions on entry, people could come and go as they pleased, and many, for various reasons, made the journey back to their usual places of abode daily. This meant that a couple of the girls who were with us managed to cadge a lift to their homes from someone or other, have a hot bath and be ready for a ride back to the festival site. I was there for just under two weeks and managed to travel daily with the girls and have a bath or a shower at their place every day.

Because of the location, the distance involved in travelling back from Glastonbury ruled out that possibility. As well as the length of time the journey would take, there was the hassle of not being able to get your vehicle back to where you wanted it, so once at Glastonbury you were stuck there. My three basic rules for anyone attending festivals are as follows: stay alive, keep clean and keep your kit together. Staying clean, I ensured that I felt comfortable, fresh and totally at ease.

Once I'd performed my ablutions, I rolled a joint and sat on the grass outside my tent. I began to think about the day ahead and how much money I would be able to make. Today and Friday were going to be the busiest for new arrivals, and I knew that, if previous years were anything to go by, there would be plenty of people coming down without tickets. My thoughts began to run away with me, and I started to think about the possibility of earning £2,000 or possibly £3,000 before Saturday afternoon came and the main rush would be over. It was still only about 6.30am, and, with thoughts of amassing a small fortune racing around my head and the new day's sun already warm, I lay down on the grass and drifted off to sleep.

CHAPTER SEVEN

It was just past nine when Billy stirred me by way of a toy kick in my ribs.

'Where did you get to last night then?' he asked, not waiting for me to wake up fully.

'Up the Green Fields,' I said, rubbing my eyes. 'It was top. What did you do?'

'Gerry and that came down. I got them all in, and they're camped up over the other side of that field over there,' he said, pointing in the appropriate direction. 'And then we all went out and ended up in some mad field somewhere, and then I just came back here and got my head down – I was done in.'

With Billy mentioning that he'd got a few of the lads from home in for nothing, my mind turned to our newfound form of employment.

'You up for a go today then or what?'

'Yeah,' Billy replied. 'I need to try and make enough to pay my debts.'

'You must have made at least a grand already. How much do you owe out then?'

'Not that much, but I want a few quid to send home to my ma, and I want to try to get myself ahead once I've paid out what I do owe.'

As Billy walked past me and into his tent, I stretched and stood up. The extra couple of hours I'd been asleep left me feeling fuzzy, and, as I extended my arms, the blood rushed to my head and made me dizzy. I sat back down on the grass.

'How long are you going to be getting ready?'

'Not long,' Billy replied. 'Skin me one up.'

As I got to work building Billy a spliff, the others began to stir, and, one by one, they appeared from where they'd been sleeping and came into the morning sunshine. Joanna and Sam's boyfriends had arrived, and, as I'd hoped, they'd met up with Ian, Jim and the two boys and brought them to our campsite. Like us, they were happy with the area in which we were staying and decided to pitch their tents alongside ours. After marking the new arrivals with a few ultraviolet stamps each, I went to see Gruff, who was sitting by the Transit.

'Still alive then,' he said mockingly.

'Too right,' I answered. 'Your missus has got some money of mine.'

Gruff laughed and retreated into the back of his van, and I went to the side of the vehicle and stooped down to the wheel under which Billy and I had hidden the previous evening's earnings. Picking up the plastic wrapper that held the cash, I opened the front door of the van and looked into the back. H must have woken up before the others because she wasn't there and was nowhere to be seen.

'And here's some more for her to look after,' I said, passing the money to Gruff. 'It's £280 from each of us. Can you give this to her when she gets back?'

'Yeah, no worries,' he said, taking the folded wad of notes. 'She's gone down with the girls to find a telephone. I'll give it to her when she gets back.'

'You OK for money?' I asked.

'Yep,' Gruff said proudly. 'So far I've only spent £1.86.'

I laughed. Both he and H always took what they needed, as they hated the idea of spending money at the festival on things that they could have brought from home.

'You sure?' I asked again and handed Gruff a £20 note. 'Here, take this for H then. Tell her to get herself something nice.'

'Cheers, Joe,' he said. 'She'll appreciate that.'

While Gruff went to the festival to watch the bands and take in the atmosphere, H loved to earn a few quid for herself. At home, she had four or five part-time jobs and was always scrimping and saving for something. One of her jobs was a few evenings a week working in an off-licence, and the owner, Jim, let her buy as much lager and spirits as she wanted at cost price. This meant that she always turned up at Glastonbury with at least twenty crates of lager, and, although Gruff worried that she might get herself into some sort of trouble, she was happy to sit at the side of one of the drags and sell passers-by loose cans. Serving them at £1.50 or sometimes £2 per can, she always did well and made herself a right few bob. Even though she was on the same thing this year, the extra money that Billy and I had been slipping her would be well-received.

I turned and went back to my tent.

'You ready yet?'

'Two minutes . . .' came the reply from Billy. 'Skin a few up.'

It was strange that. While words such as 'haggis', 'kilt', 'bag-pipes', 'Rangers' and 'Celtic' were terms that were well known for coming from Scotland, the language that came out of Billy's parti-cular part of the Strathclyde district always included the expression 'skin up'. It didn't matter. Since meeting our taxi driver, we'd learned that he had a plentiful supply of blow, and, after we'd intro-duced ourselves to him and taken advantage of the use of his motorbike to get us to Gate 2, he let us know that if we ran short of a smoke he'd be willing to sort us out.

By the time Billy was ready, I'd rolled up ten joints and, after giving him five of them, stashed the other four in my top pocket and lit one for the journey. We walked into the camp next to ours, found our taxi and within minutes were once again on our way to Gate 2.

With the festival proper starting on Friday, the volume of people turning up was increasing by the hour. Both Billy and myself were kept extremely busy, occasionally stamping groups of ten or more, but more often than not helping three or four at a time gain entry. The layout of Gate 2 was slightly different from that of Gate 3, in as much as there was a slope down towards the turnstiles from the perimeter road. Although it wasn't much of an incline, it was enough to take it out of you when climbing it umpteen times an hour. As well as that, there was a certain disadvantage to this point of entry, as the stewards manning the gates were able to see the road from where they were stationed and would be able to watch our every movement. After a certain amount of time, they were bound to become suspicious.

After working the gate for some three hours, we decided to have a well-earned rest and took a trip into the festival. Entering through Gate 2 and walking down the hill along Muddy Lane, the path that would eventually meet Babylon, we turned left and went to the Meeting Point, which was a five-minute walk along the drag. There, we turned right and chose to sit down at a table outside a catering outlet that was on the way to the Green Fields. As I grabbed a seat and reserved another for Billy, he went up to the counter and ordered. Returning with our food and drinks, he sat alongside me, and we said nothing for ten minutes as we tucked in. Finishing off his drink, Billy started to talk about how we'd been doing so far and how much we might end up making by the time the festival ended.

At home my main source of income came from serving up sixteenths, eighths and quarters of hash, but by the time I'd laid on deals to my mates or smoked more of it than I was selling, I usually ended up owing my dealer a fair few quid. Now, however, the money I had made from getting people into the festival had already earned me enough to cover the quite considerable bill that I owed. It would also give me the chance to buy a good amount from him with cash up front, an arrangement that would not only see me get the gear at a cheaper price but also give me the chance to make a bigger profit.

'If we keep on like we're doing till tonight,' Billy enthused, 'I reckon we could earn ourselves two grand each at least – that's what I want anyway.'

'Me, too,' I replied. 'What we've done so far is brilliant, but I want to keep going as long as I can.'

Our conversation was cut short momentarily as a black guy asked us to move along the bench we were on so he could sit down between us.

Motioning towards Billy, I said, 'Sorry, mate, we're together.'

'Sorry, bruv,' he replied, and instead of taking a seat alongside of us, he went around to the other side of the table and sat opposite. The interruption was enough for us to lower the tone of our voices, but, nevertheless, we carried on with our conversation, and it returned to how much we both owed various drug suppliers and the like at home, and in our minds we were both already spending what we thought we'd make. We smoked a joint each, rolled another, and left the comfort and shade of the café to head towards Gate 3 and another few hours of graft.

The sun was now blazing down, the punters were coming in thick and fast and everything was great. We were both well on the way to reaching the targets we'd set ourselves to earn from working the stamp, and life was sweet. A few more of our mates had turned up, and, after getting them in, we went to do our bit by helping them set their tents up and generally settle in. I was, though, totally preoccupied with the idea of making money, and the constant nagging thought at the back of my mind was of all those people without tickets who were desperate to get into the festival and were gaining entry via means other than through Billy and myself.

I wanted to be in two places at once, both working the stamp but also having a laugh with the rest of the chaps who'd just arrived. I knew that I was putting myself under pressure by working all the hours that I could, but the lure of earning what was easy money was well and truly under my skin. It was as though I'd been hooked by the strongest drug at the festival. After an hour or so with the new arrivals, I decided I was going back to work. Leaving our mates' encampment, I headed for Gate 3.

I arrived at the access point to find that it was packed full of ticket touts and others offering various methods of entry including one with an ultraviolet pen. I knew our scam wouldn't remain exclusive for the duration of the festival, but when I saw someone else on the same trick as us I was pretty sick about it. Nevertheless, there were only two choices as far as the stamp was concerned. Give up or carry on, and, for me at least, it was the second of the two options.

Billy had decided to stay back up at the camp, and I was working it myself. When he said he wasn't going to come with me, I'd already made my mind up to go, and I have to admit that the thought of being unaccompanied this time left me with butterflies in my stomach. It meant that, as well as not having someone to watch my back, I'd have to be doubly on my toes and risked getting turned over by either a punter or another scammer, or even getting my head kicked in.

I decided to stick to groups of four or less and only approached after I'd given them a thorough once-over. Even though I was operating single-handedly, it was going well, and my nervousness soon wore off as I concentrated on making money. After about two hours I'd earned myself another £150, which I was more than happy with, and decided to keep going until I had another £450. If I achieved this target, I would put £500 away and have £100 to spend.

It was getting towards early evening now, and things were more busy. There was a never-ending stream of people looking to get in, and, for me, business was brisk. I was now averaging £10 to £15 per person – I'd gone down on my asking price, as it seemed there were more people working on getting others in than there were punters. I was also doing deals with people who weren't quite sure of me. If there were four together, I was charging them £30, or £7.50 per head, which was, for the takers at least, extremely good value.

Loads of people I asked were, quite rightly, suspicious of me and didn't want to know. That is, until they found out how much others were charging and heard the tales of people getting ripped off. After that, it was a case of me sitting on the side of the path with my customers sitting opposite, their arms in front of my hands. I would draw three or four circles on their forearms with the ultra-violet pen, smudge them by rubbing with my forearm and, as I was doing that, I'd repeat the now usual punch line, 'Have a nice time.'

This seemed to relax them a bit, although in the majority of cases, until they were safely through the gates, they were very nervous. It might have been the thought of getting caught – or the fact that I usually offered to carry their bags through for them, and they had half a mind that I was going to do a runner with their kit – that made them feel uneasy. That idea never entered my mind, and anyway, it was a festival, and I believed in good karma, and if I started ripping people off bad things would happen to me. I wasn't that hard-hearted or mean.

After a couple or so hours I stopped for a rest. By this time I wanted to count up how much I'd earned but couldn't get any cash out in public. I must have got around about fifty or so people into the festival during this little spell, but I wasn't keeping count on exactly how many or how much I'd made. I headed back to my tent, and, once there, I rolled a joint, sat down and totalled up. After counting the money then counting it again, I found that I was short of the £600 I'd wanted by £190, but with what H had stashed away for me, I now had just over £1,300. Leaving myself with a £10 note in my pocket, I hid the rest of the money under the van, had a wash and made my way back towards Gate 3.

As I walked down the path, I could see a vaguely familiar figure coming towards me. It was Frankie Burns, who, after an afternoon in one of our hometown local pubs had, on a whim, decided to make the trek to Glastonbury. He'd had four or five pints too many, gone home for a sleeping bag and scrounged a lift from someone who'd been good natured enough to put up with him for a near two-hour journey to the edge of the festival site. Now here he was bowling along, still half-cut, with the sleeping bag he had draped over his shoulders making him look like Batman. Because it was his first time at Glastonbury, he was clueless as to where he was meant to be going or, indeed, where everybody that he knew would be. He was lucky that I ran into him.

'Alright, Frank?' I said, as I wandered up to him.

'Where's everybody else?' he slurred, his legs nearly buckling as he tried to stand still.

'They're probably out and about,' I replied. 'Who'd you come here with?'

'Tony and Ella gave us a lift,' he responded, his Glaswegian accent accentuating his already almost incomprehensible speech.

'Is that right you can get us in for nuthin'?'

'Yeah, no problem, Frank, but I think I'd better take you up to where we're staying and leave you there for a bit. Give you a chance to get your head together.'

'Aye, alright. But can you get me in for nuthin'?'

'I'll get you to where everybody is camping, and I'll stamp you up, Frank. Someone will be back soon, and they can sort you out for taking you in. You're in no fit state right now . . .'

With that, we walked up to where Gerry, Keyo and the rest of their crew where staying. I stamped Frank's arm several times and waited until he'd drifted off to sleep before I left him. As I made my way back to Gate 3, I couldn't help but chuckle at both the way that he had turned up and also at the state he was in. I wondered what he'd be thinking when he sobered up and found himself at Glaston-bury, and I also wondered what the lads at whose camp I'd left him would make of it when they returned and found another body added to their number.

The evening's darkness again brought a change to both the general atmosphere outside Gate 3 and the festival itself. With the

approaching dusk came a feeling of having to be extra cautious. Not just in case of getting lost or losing those you were with – a phenomenon that happened frequently – but people were also worried about being victims of the many muggers, thieves and con artists. Personally, I wasn't that concerned. I knew where to go and, more importantly, how to find my way back to my tent and where my friends would be. I was, though, wary of losing the money I had earned, and I was still wearing my money-belt around my waist just in case.

The area around Gate 3 reminded me of a refugee camp that I must have, at some point, seen on the television news. Groups of people hanging around with their bags, rucksacks and tents, the majority of them looking lost. These were the people who'd arrived at the festival totally unaware of the hassle they'd face trying to get in for nothing.

Although the routes in through the holes under the fence or over it via ladders were open to them, their bags and tents made such means of entry unviable. To use these options, they had to be light on their feet to avoid the risk of getting caught by the security squads that were now, if the rumours were to be believed, dishing out beatings to those they caught.

Most of the people outside the gate looking for a cheap way in were of a peaceable disposition, just wanted to get into the festival and enjoy a few joints and see some of the bands. Not many wanted to get involved in an argument, let alone a fight, with the security teams. Neither did they want anything to do with those who were obviously looking to exploit them by way of a dodgy drug deal or by taking money on the false promise of entry. There were several people offering stamps with ultraviolet pens, but, fortunately for me, they were asking what I considered stupid money – £30 and £40 – and they weren't getting much trade. The thing they had going for them, though, was that they were well mobbed-up and seemed to be working in groups of no less than eight or nine.

This left me vulnerable to attack and a good pasting from those who now looked upon the area as their patch. To be caught by any of them was something I didn't want to happen, especially as this was the nearest entrance to where I was camped. If I got myself into any trouble with anyone, I would run the risk of being seen every time I went in or out of the festival.

Looking for business single-handedly, I was again very selective in the people I approached, mainly asking couples or groups that were made up of both males and females. After a couple of hours I had earned another £250, but, because I was on my own, finding the passing trade wasn't as easy as it had been working with Billy.

A team of ticket touts were now in front of the gate and openly plying their trade. 'I'll buy or sell any tickets,' shouted a black guy with a Brummie accent. He was with three others who were white and who also sounded like they came from Birmingham. I don't know what it was about them and how many there were dotted about elsewhere, but their appearance in some strange way altered the rules of what was going down on the business front.

The people who were mobbed-up in crews and previously having a bit of everything were now concentrating on trying to get rid of the various chemical substances that would earn them much more than an entrance fee, and were they doing exactly what they'd come to Glastonbury to do.

That left the touts to buy and sell tickets and three or four other groups of assorted travellers, scallies and chancers working on getting people in via their version of the stamp or over or under the fence. Between them, they were setting the recognised and accepted market price of dubious entry to Glastonbury. The touts, as they do, were giving people stupidly little money for spare tickets and asking ridiculously high prices of those who wanted to buy them. They seemed to be doing well, with at least four or five tickets on display in their hands at any one time, leaving the other grafters charging

40s and 50s for their services. And then there was me . . . and it was time I put my prices up.

Even though it was now past 9pm, there was a constant flow of people making their way down the hill from the camping fields outside the perimeter and from the road that led into that side of the festival, and it was bringing loads of business with it.

While the others were happy to get punters into the gig right in front of the entrance, I preferred to pick up my trade on the hill at Ridgy Ground. Waiting for the people I thought might be trying to get in and thought looked likely and willing customers, I'd begin the banter.

Standing on the side of the path, and as people were just within hearing distance, I'd half whisper, 'You OK for getting in?'

Most people were, in a very British sort of way, very polite. 'Sorted, thanks, mate' or 'We've got tickets' or 'We've been in already' were the most frequent responses.

I asked a couple and got a negative response, but two people walking alongside them slowed their pace. I looked in their direction.

'Hello, girls. You OK for getting in?'

No reply.

'Have you got tickets?'

The blonde one gave her mate a look, but they walked on. I followed and went up beside the girl with black, curly, shoulder-length hair.

'Look, I'm not being funny with ya, but I'm the guy you need to see if you ain't got a way in. There's some proper horrors down there . . .'

Blondie stopped and held her friend's arm to stop her. After a few seconds of whispered conversation, the fairer of the two turned to me.

'How much, and how can you get us in?' she said in a husky, well-spoken accent.

'Fifteen each.'

She looked at her friend.

'It's up to you,' said the girl with the dark hair, betraying a hint of a Mancunian twang.

She gave her friend a sideways glance, turned back towards me, half closed her eyes and looked down as she nodded.

Addressing them both, I asked, 'Where's your bags?'

They looked at each other a little nervously.

'The thing is,' I continued, 'I don't want to be walking miles with you to go and get your stuff.'

'We've got some friends looking after them just up there,' replied the northerner. 'If we get in, we'll come back and get them.'

I motioned with my head for them to follow me, and we stepped to one side of the path and squatted down in front of an empty parked-up motor. I explained the workings of the official security system and the reason for using the ultraviolet pen and how I'd get them in before taking any payment. I said what all the others who were grafting the gate were doing and how much they were charging and also that they were a rip-off bunch of thieving scum-bags whose number probably included some violent rapists. Once that was out in the open, the two girls had no other choice but to try to get in with me, seeing as they'd been fortunate enough to run into the only honest and, at only £15 each, cheapest bunker-inner working Gate 3.

The one with black hair looked at me, then at her friend and finally back at me.

'OK, we'll try it. What do we do?'

'Look, the first thing is, I've got to stamp you. Roll your sleeve up and hold your arm out.'

Moving around so as my back was to the path to shield what I was doing, I held her wrist with one hand and drew a circle on her forearm with my other. I repeated the design a couple of times and then, as I smudged them, I looked her in the eyes.

'Have a nice time.'

Her eyes narrowed, but she giggled nervously, portraying a cute smile.

'Your turn,' I said, looking at her friend.

She put her arm in front of mine, the ritual was repeated and we were off.

As we walked down the hill towards the gate at the bottom, those plying their trade became more evident.

'Want to get in?' said a guy aged about twenty, who looked like a proper crusty, his mousy fair hair shaved tight to his skin on the side of his head but with dreadlocks growing from the top and back of his skull reaching his shoulders and resting on a studded-leather biker's jacket.

'Sweet, bruv,' I answered quickly, as I manoeuvred my way between the two girls and linked arms with them so I could guide them past and through the opposition. 'We've been in already.'

He went on, 'Want any Es?'

'We're sorted for everything, cheers, mate,' I said, this time staring him straight in the eyes and slowing the pace at which the girls and I were walking.

He looked at me and at the girls. They gave him their best *fuck off, you idiot* glares, and as we walked on he turned and went back towards those walking past him, repeating his pitch.

'Es for sale!' This time the voice came from a black guy, standing at the side of the path with six or seven of his mates in close attendance.

Keeping a firm grip on the two girls, I continued straight past, head down with my eyes hidden by the peak of my baseball cap, saying nothing, but I was making sure that I was checking as many of the other main players' faces as I could.

We walked on and reached the gate.

'Watch me, and just do what I do,' I told the pair I was escorting. 'Stay cool, and you'll be laughing.'

I led the way with the two girls following closely. We presented our forearms to the stewards who, after giving them the usual examination, waved us through. The delight and excitement of the girls was obvious, but they kept their composure and walked on the hundred or so yards to where the path to the festival turned and where we would be out of the way of the eyes of the stewards.

'Thanks, mate,' the blonde one said, looking into the purse she had in her hands. 'Thirty for both of us?'

'That's right, lovely. Make sure you take care and have a great time,' I answered, smiling and nodding gratefully as she passed me the money. As I was about to turn away, the dark-haired one motioned for me to stop.

'Can you help us get our friends in?'

Having gained confidence in me, the girls then went on to explain that there were eleven of their friends waiting outside at the top of the hill who had yet to gain entry. After negotiating a fee of £150 for the lot, the girls and I walked back out through the gate which we'd just passed through and into the stream of people coming in.

Crossing the lane and heading back up to Ridgy Ground, the same faces were still offering their services. Walking straight past, I kept my head down low and squeezed in between the girls. I was doing my best to take no chances, so I wouldn't be sussed, but the more I kept going back and forth through Gate 3 the greater the chance was that someone or other might work out that I was up to something.

The pair I'd just taken through led me up to where their friends were waiting and explained who I was and how I could help. Because of their number, it took me three separate trips to get them all in, and, once they had been stamped up and taken through the gate and paid me their dues, I considered whether I should either pack it in for the night or continue working, but somewhere else.

Thinking some more about it, I decided to stay on the festival side of the gate, sit down, roll a joint and then work out what my next move would be. Everybody I knew who was at the festival would be having a ball, either getting stoned, be tripping their heads off on acid or getting drunk, but I was enjoying a real buzz from earning easy money. Sitting about fifty yards beyond the entrance to the gate, I could see lots of potential customers going up to where the stewards were, have a look and then walk away, all seemingly despondent and at a loss as to how they were going to get in. There was a fortune to be made.

Nevertheless, and despite the potential money that I could have earned there, after smoking the joint right down to the roach, I decided to leave Gate 3 and made my way up to Gate 2 through the festival. The route took me past the children's field on my right, down through Babylon along the Stage Road drag and then up to the right along Muddy Lane to where I hoped there would be some more punters and fewer people likely to beat the crap out of me or have me over if I was sussed for what I was doing.

After walking for some fifteen minutes, I exited Gate 2, and, in the dim light provided by the security floodlights, I could see some prospective customers lurking very conspicuously at the top of the short incline that led away from the festival. There was a group of eight teenagers, students probably, who were looking somewhat lost and a little bedraggled. I approached, giving them the usual patter and, after the by now usual initial response, managed to negotiate a price of £120 for the lot.

Fortunately the distance between the entrance and where this group stood was no more than about a hundred yards, so it wasn't too much hassle for me to go in and out three times to help them through. Although I was receiving some quizzical looks from the stewards manning the gate, their glances didn't bother me, as I was confident they hadn't worked out what I was doing.

I now had over £600 on me, and, being on my own and with the night passing quickly, I decided to head back to the camp to drop the money off. Instead of walking through the festival, I went along the lanes, turning right at the top of the entrance to Gate 2 and traversing the path that ran alongside the perimeter fence. It was pitch black in places, so dark that sometimes, if it hadn't been for the chatter of people talking as they were walking along, I would have quite literally bumped into them.

The lack of light, although somewhat scary, did have its advantages in as much as any potential robbers would have trouble identifying their targets, although on several occasions I walked straight off the path and into the bushes and foliage that lined the route.

Every now and again a car or a van would pass, the vehicles coming from both directions and, when the headlamps shone down the path, I made my way along as quickly as I could and took advantage of being able to see, even if it only gained me a few seconds on my journey back to where I was camped.

After twenty-five minutes I was at the point where Cockmill Lane met the entrance to Gate 3, and by the time I got there it was as busy as I had ever seen it. There were no stewards and a definite air of tension in the area, what with the mix of drug sellers, those promising passage into the festival and loads of people without tickets.

Not bothering to immerse myself in what was going on, I made my way straight up the hill to where I was staying, sat down and rolled a joint. There was no one from my lot there, but, even so, I felt safe and secure, especially as the first thing I'd done was stash my money under the wheels of H's van. As I smoked my joint, I reflected upon the money I had made so far and weighed up how much, potentially at least, I could take home if I kept earning at the same rate.

I now had £1,900 put away, what with the £600 I'd made that

evening and the £1,300 H was looking after. With tomorrow being Friday and perhaps the busiest day for new arrivals, I estimated that I could, if I worked hard enough, earn myself another £1,000 at least. That meant I would have roughly £3,000 to go home with, and there was still Saturday to come. Things were looking rosy.

Using the light from the torch suspended from a piece of string attached to the roof of the inside of my tent, I rolled another joint to smoke and one to keep for later and toyed with the idea of going into the festival to look for the others. I'd hardly seen Gruff or H since we'd arrived and thought that a change from what I'd been doing would do me some good, but with tens of thousands of people at the festival, and without any idea where they'd decided to go, I stood little chance of running into them. Even so, I got myself ready for a trek down to Babylon for a mooch in the hope that, at some point, I might meet Billy or some other friendly faces.

As I made my way back across Ridgy Ground and down the hill towards Gate 3, the beat of the festival was thumping in regular 4/4 time, with the view from the incline encompassing the furthest reaches of the boundaries and beyond. There was a haze that seemed to blur what light was emanating from the drags, the stalls, the stages and the campfires, and this gave the whole place a magical, mysterious and yet somewhat intimidating aura. It gave me butterflies in the pit of my stomach and, although it was something I had experienced before, that feeling in my gut always put me slightly on edge, and even to this day, when I think about that view of Glastonbury, it always sends shivers down my spine.

Walking through the no-man's land that was the lane at the entrance to Gate 3, I saw a couple who looked like they didn't have any tickets and were stuck for getting in. I had the tools the trade required and couldn't resist. After giving them my spiel and seeing them through the gate, I had another £40 in my pocket, and the lure of making some more easy money made me decide to abandon my quest to find my mates in favour of working the stamp for a bit longer.

By the time it got to midnight I had amassed another £350, £300 of which was stashed in my money-belt, the pocket to which was in front of my abdomen between my skin and boxer shorts, with my jeans keeping it securely in place. By then I'd had enough of working and made my mind up to get back to the camp, drop off the cash and get down to the festival and make my way towards the Green Fields for something to eat, a hot cup of tea and, hopefully, some nice company.

As I made my way along the lane and was about to turn towards the incline that led to my camp, I came across four guys who, like all my previous customers, looked like they didn't have a way into the festival. Approaching them, I offered my services, and we negotiated a price of £70. As I stamped them, they gave me the money up front, and I put it straight into my jeans pocket. I turned to lead them down to the festival but was suddenly aware of three black guys who were pushing their way past my four customers and straight towards me. One of them grabbed my right arm. As I tried to pull it away, another said, 'Don't try it . . .'

I was being had off.

The four I was trying to get in immediately leaped to my defence. One, a Rastafarian, tried to step in between me and the one who had hold of my arm.

'What ya doin', mon? Leave him. His tryin' to do us a favour.'

I knew what was happening alright, but, as the Rasta and one of the others I'd just stamped was also black, I thought I might have a chance of getting out of the situation. For a moment it looked as if the Rasta's appeal had been successful. The one holding my arm let go, and I went to walk away with my four customers. However, my freedom only lasted a few seconds.

In the murk of the night, I could see that one of the three who was mugging me was holding a baseball bat, and he looked ready to hit me with it. Another flashed a knife right in front of my face and the third, the biggest, opened his jacket, reached inside and, pulling out a handgun, waved it under my nose and said, 'Don't fuck with us and you won't get this . . . OK?'

CHAPTER EIGHT

The four people I had just stamped were powerless to help me and backed off, the fear in their eyes clearly visible. One of the black guys looked shocked.

'I'm sorry, man . . .' he said, before he and his three mates walked rapidly away. Now it was just me and the three tooled-up muggers.

Somehow I managed to remain composed. I don't know whether it was adrenalin or too much puff, but, whatever it was, my thoughts were clear and calm. Two of my attackers took one of my arms each and held them behind my back while the third guy started to search me. Arms, legs, jeans and jacket pockets all got a good feel, and the money and pen were soon discovered and confiscated. While I was gutted that I'd been captured and had £120 taken from me, I was consoled by the fact that they hadn't found the money-belt, which was still hidden next to my crotch.

While the guy with the knife held my right hand and the one with the bat held my left, the biggest of the three with the handgun grabbed me by my coat collar, pulled me towards him and, pointing the pistol he was holding at my face before pushing the barrel of it against my temple, growled, 'You're coming this way.'

Although I'd only caught a quick sight of the gun, it looked like a Walther PPK, a piece that had been given worldwide attention in the 007 films as British secret agent James Bond's weapon of choice. It was a semi-automatic that had been produced for both military and domestic police use in several countries and had been available for decades. Although I wasn't sure that the gun was real – it might well have been a replica – in those few moments when my assailant had made sure I'd seen it, the weapon looked convincing, and I was positive he wasn't messing about.

While the thought of being shot didn't appeal, neither did getting stabbed with the knife. It had a blade about eight inches long with a cutting edge on one side, a serrated edge on the other and a hole in the middle. It really looked like it could do some damage.

I was thinking rationally, but the overwhelming thought in my mind was that if these guys were going to kill me, I hoped they'd make it quick with a gunshot to my head rather than what I thought might be a painful, slow and lingering death by being stabbed or beaten with the baseball bat.

Seeing that I was compliant and offering no resistance, the gun and the knife were concealed by their owners, and I was then frogmarched away from the entrance to the gate and along the lane to the left of the incline that led to where I was camping. I was being prodded in the back by something and, although I initially thought it might be the gun, it was the baseball bat being pushed into my spine. We walked for a couple of minutes before stopping next to a clearing in the bushes that separated the path from the fence.

Although the lane was dark, there was some light coming from within the festival boundary, its source being one of the security watchtowers that had been erected at various points along the fence, the distance between each being several hundred yards. We were about fifty yards to the left of one, the radiance of the bulb from the lookout point illuminating the immediate vicinity and creating a dim glow for several yards beyond.

In the gloom I could see that the three who'd had me off looked like archetypal hoodies, the clothes they were wearing the same as any other streetwise black youth from the inner city. The two with the bat and the knife sported baseball caps and looked like they were about twenty-five years old, and both were dressed in polo shirts, tracksuits and smart trainers. They had plaited dreadlocks protruding from the back of their headwear and stood about six feet tall, looked like they weighed about eleven stone.

Had any one of them been on their own, I would have fancied my chances in a one-to-one fight, but the guy with the gun was bigger, standing about six foot three and weighing at least fourteen stone, and the weapon he was holding put me off trying anything that might have made my predicament worse than it already was. He had close-cropped hair, and, although his bulk was covered by the blue-and-white Fila tracksuit top and bottoms he was wearing, it was obvious he was extremely well-built and looked like he could easily fill the part of a doorman.

The three of them were each wearing the obligatory thick gold chain around their necks and had gold sovereign rings on their fingers and gold bracelets hanging from their wrists. My first impression was that they were of West Indian descent, and, judging from their accents, I estimated the chances were that they probably came from south London and their main source of income was the distribution of illicit drugs.

'Where's yer fuckin' gear?' the big guy demanded.

'I've got none.'

'I ain't gonna ask you again.'

'I ain't got none,' I repeated, adding, 'except for a bit of blow . . . personal . . .'

The one with the bat started sniggering and let it slip from his grasp and hang from his wrist by a string loop tied around the handle. As the string went taut, he lifted his arm and swung the bat around his wrist for one turn before catching it and then waving it in a sweeping motion in front of my face, its tip missing my nose by a couple of inches.

'Wanna know somefing, white boy?' the one with the shooter continued. 'We ain't fuckin' about with you – we know what you been at – we've been working this stretch, and you been creaming it now for at least a day. Wanna know somefing, white boy? We've been watchin' you. You been stealin' our customers. You been stealin' from us!'

The other two moved closer. This could be it, I thought, although somehow I kept calm. 'I ain't been stealing nothing,' I retorted, looking straight at him. 'I've been doing my own thing.'

He looked at me straight in the eyes, his own narrowing as his facial features seemed to change from a look of anger to one of intrigue. 'Oh yeah? Start talking.'

'I've just been helping get a few people in.' I shrugged my shoulders. 'That's all.'

His voice seemed to go up in pitch. 'And just how you been doin' that then?'

I stared straight back at him trying to put on an air of defiance, but at the same time I realised that to save myself from getting smashed everywhere and proper done over I'd have to compromise myself in as much as I'd have go some way to telling them what the scam was.

Before I could say anything, he said, 'And don't say getting people in through a hole in the fence. I haven't seen you go near it the whole time I've been watchin' you.'

A thought flashed through my mind that I should try to tell him that I had someone on the gate and was working with them, but, as the other two looked like they were hungry for a kill and I was their dinner, I thought I'd be best just being honest and see where that got me.

'You've been in and out a few times, haven't you?' I said, looking at the main guy and trying to ignore the one with the bat. 'How've you been doing it?'

'What you on about?' He spat. 'How have I been doin' what?'

'Getting in and out of the festival. How do the people on the gate know that you've already been in?'

'They look at the pass-out stamp —'

He was about to continue, but I cut in, 'I've been drawing

them on with an ultraviolet pen. Your buddy there's got it,' I said, nodding towards the guy with the knife.

'Show!' he said, as the knifeman produced the pen from his pocket and gave it to him.

'How, exactly, have you been doin' this then?'

I held out my hand and he passed the pen to me. I rolled up my sleeve and, with my right hand, drew a circle on my left inside forearm. Smudging it with my right wrist, I showed it to him.

The knifeman took a look. 'I can't see nothing. He's chattin' shit.'

Suppressing a laugh that was, no doubt, in part down to nerves, I said, 'You're not meant to see anything. That's the whole point.'

In the dim light coming from above the fence, I could see that the other two were smiling at the knifeman's stupidity while he looked awkward and embarrassed.

'You say this works?' the big guy continued before looking to the knifeman and saying, 'Go get Delroy.'

Obeying orders without question, he departed, heading back down the lane in the direction of Gate 3. As he disappeared into the blackness of the lane, I immediately thought of trying to escape, but my two remaining captors seemed to read my mind with the one holding the bat again swinging it perilously close to my face. If I'd run, who's to say that I wouldn't have got ten yards and felt a bullet in my back? The big geezer didn't think twice about showing me his shooter, and, judging by the way that they were treating me, they didn't look like they gave a fuck about what happened to anyone who crossed their path.

He gestured with the first finger of his left hand, as if to say, *Give it here.* 'Pen,' he said quietly and held out his right hand for me to return it to him. 'So how much you been making then? You looked like you were proper busy when I was spyin'.'

'A couple of quid here and there . . .'

He paused and inhaled. 'How much?' he demanded, his tone slightly more menacing.

'Fifteens, sometimes twenties,' I replied. 'Depends on the situation.'

'Situation? Situation?' he repeated. 'This is the fuckin' situation. You're gonna show me how that thing works for real, and then I'll decide what to do with you. Do you get me?'

Taking a deep breath, I replied, 'Yeah, I get ya.'

The big guy crouched down on his haunches and motioned me to do the same. His sidekick followed suit as we waited for his mate – the knifeman – to come back. Within a couple of minutes or so he returned with another three black youths, all of who looked like they were 100 per cent streetwise but, nevertheless, somewhat confused by the event that was Glastonbury.

However big people were, however much they think they had seen, I've never met a single person who was, on their first visit, not overwhelmed by the sheer scale of the Glastonbury Festival and the sights and different types of people who were there. This lot were from some inner-city urban jungle where they probably owned their own patch, and everybody living within it or even just travelling through gave them respect. Here, at Glastonbury, there weren't many people bothered about that type of crap, with taking notice of their city habits and pecking order. It was easy to tell they'd never been to a gig quite like this before.

The big guy called one of the three who'd just arrived to him, and, addressing the youth but looking at me, he said, 'He gonna draw you your stamp on your arm. He gonna take his pen and put the mark right where you want it.' Pausing for a second, his accent then went from what sounded like a London brogue to Jamaican. 'Don't be frightened now, Delroy,' he continued. 'If he am an batty boy, your brethren here to look after you, ya know.'

Everybody else except me and Delroy laughed. I just blinked slowly while Delroy recovered from his embarrassment and was half shoved towards me by the funny man. He handed me the pen. I turned my right arm and wrist to indicate to Delroy that he should do the same, and he extended his arm towards me. As I held his lower arm to steady it, one of the others sniggered.

'Shut it,' said the big man in no uncertain manner. Not a peep.

I drew the circle, twisted his arm in the direction of my right hand and smudged it. Repeating the action three more times before releasing my grip, I looked him in the eyes. 'Have a nice time,' I said quietly and almost to myself, feeling somewhat reticent, but there was no reaction. He stood back two paces and looked at his leader.

Again gesturing with his finger, he called the other two who'd helped him mug me over to where he was standing. Turning away, he whispered his instructions to them before turning back and talking to Delroy and me. Dropping the Jamaican patois and returning to a London accent, he gave us his orders.

'You two gonna go down together with Carlton and Duane and see if this thing works and then come back up to me.' Addressing Carlton and Duane but looking at me he continued, 'And make sure our new friend don't decide to try to leave us.' Giving me a look that indicated evil intention, he underlined what he meant by adding, 'D'ya get me?'

As I looked past him, Carlton – the guy with the bat – held one end of the weapon and smacked the other end into the palm of his free hand, the leather glove he was now wearing taking the impact and softening the blow.

Delroy, my two minders and me then turned down the track towards the gate. As we walked away from the others, I thought about trying to run, but we were facing downhill towards the gate and into the light. With three chasing me, I didn't think I'd have that good a chance of getting away, and to run back up the path would mean going past the spot where the big guy and the rest of his mates were waiting for us to return. I reasoned that I should just carry on as I had been doing, cooperating with them, see where it took me and draw another breath. There were a thousand thoughts racing through my mind, but there was one that bothered me more than the rest. The big man said that he'd been watching me for a couple of days, and I wondered whether they'd followed me back to where Billy, Gruff, H and the others were.

My thoughts were cut short by a tap on the right shoulder. I stopped walking and turned. Duane and Carlton looked at me and then down to their hands which were at waist level. The pair of them now each had a blade in their right hands. There was no need for them to tell me what would happen if I tried anything stupid. Then Carlton, his baseball bat now secreted in the waist of his tracksuit bottoms, spoke.

'What's happening now is this. Duane is gonna go into the queue first, Delroy second, you third and I'll be right on your shoulder.'

'Wait,' I replied, looking at Delroy. 'I should go ahead of him, show him exactly what to do. It's the way I've been working it.'

Carlton looked at Duane. 'I'm watchin' your back.' He then looked at me. 'No foolin' round now. Remember, I'm on ya.'

With that, we turned into the entrance for Gate 3. In single file, one behind the other, we joined a queue to get in, with me following Duane, Delroy behind me and with Carlton in close attendance bringing up the rear. As I had done each time I'd got people in, I exaggerated my arm movement towards the steward operating the ultraviolet light, making sure that Delroy saw me do it. He looked nervous but had no need to be, as his stamp passed a cursory inspection without question. We reached the end of the run of metal barriers, and both Carlton and Duane, motioning to Delroy and me, turned to head back out.

'Where ya goin'?' I said firmly, the three somewhat taken aback that I had the temerity to ask them what they were doing. Duane's hand went inside his jacket, his demeanour immediately making me think that he was reaching for his blade.

'Think about it,' I said quickly. 'It will look suss if you walk straight back out. It ain't busy enough to do that right now.' As they stopped, I pointed to the bend in the track that, once traversed, would give a person the first sight of what was to come inside the festival arena.

'Just walk around there for a minute, just in case there are any eyes on us. I've been in and out for three days now.'

Duane looked at Carlton. With the two of them pleased that Delroy had got in without a problem, they suddenly seemed a little more relaxed when it came to dealing with me, and they agreed that it made good sense. We walked around the corner, stood for a couple of minutes and then turned back. Just as we entered the line of metal barriers on the exit side, I turned to Delroy and reminded him to get several official stamps on the other arm.

'Won't they say anything if I ask for more than one?'

I laughed.

'Try to clock my arm when I go through, you'll see what I mean.'

As we approached the stewards and I held out my arm for a stamp.

'Try to find a place where I haven't got one please,' I asked politely. 'I'm worried that the ones I have got already are merging into each other.'

'Let's have a look then,' said a girl in a yellow luminous bib as she took my wrist and held my arm up to the ultraviolet light. I motioned Delroy forward, and as the purple light fell on my forearm, there was just a blur of ink all the way up. As I glanced at Delroy, he cracked a slight smile.

She laughed.

'When did you get here then? It looks like you've been here for a month.'

'Got here Tuesday,' I replied. 'Been helping all my friends get in and out . . . you know.'

She laughed again before saying, 'What about one on the back of your wrist? That looks quite clear.'

I offered her my right hand.

'That'll do nicely. Thanks.'

With that she stamped the back of my hand, and I held it up to the light. It was there, nice and clear.

Delroy offered his left arm, the one I hadn't stamped. He stared at the girl with no visible emotion.

'Give him a couple or three please,' I said. 'He's only got here tonight.'

Again the girl laughed and duly obliged, the coloured light shining down upon three freshly printed stamps and another faint smile of satisfaction teased his face. My minders and I then made our way back up the lane to where their friends were waiting. When we got there, all eyes were on Delroy and then on me. Delroy simply nodded his head in the direction of the big guy, who, after hearing his name mentioned by one of his crew, I now knew was called Alex. He turned to look at me and then the two others that had come with Delroy. He motioned them to come towards him and said to roll up their sleeves. He then proceeded to draw some circles on their arms and told Delroy to take them down to the gate and go in. He and his two mates then left, but were back within four or five minutes.

'It didn't work,' Delroy said angrily. 'Mine was OK, but they were stopped.'

The other two shrugged their shoulders.

'Come,' said Alex, looking at me, 'and tell me what's occurring.'

I shrugged my shoulders.

'You must have done it wrong,' I offered.

He looked quizzically at me.

'How d'ya mean?'

I held out my hand and he gave me the pen. I looked at the two that had been knocked back and they both extended their arms.

Ensuring I chose the ones that their leader hadn't, I drew a few stamps on their arms and made sure I smudged them. Both times I repeated the mantra, 'Have a nice time.'

'Just make sure you go past a different steward,' I said, as they turned away from the group and headed towards the gate.

Within another seven or eight minutes they were back and smiling, having gained entry with no problem then each acquiring several official stamps on the way out. Alex looked at me.

'Why didn't it work when I did it?'

'Like I said, you might have done it wrong.'

'Come, we try some more.'

With that, he signalled everybody to follow him, indicating to Duane and Carlton that they should once again keep their eyes on me to stop me escaping. We walked back down towards the gate, but, instead of turning right and into the festival at the junction or left up the hill, we headed along Cockmill Lane following the perimeter fence. As we continued and passed people going in the opposite direction, the group spread out with a couple of the younger ones whispering 'Es' to any potential buyer.

Two girls approached, Lancashire by the sound of their accents. 'Es?'

'You don't know where the hole in the fence is, do you?' said one.

I was about to speak but bit my tongue. Alex stepped forward.

'You want to get in, girls?' he said very politely but with that little bit of street accent that was enough to make people uneasy. He continued. 'I got me a nice little trick here to get you both in, no holes under the fence, no climbing over but straight through the front door. You interested?'

The girl who'd asked the original question glanced at her friend. They were both sheepish. In the shadows, I could now see the features of the first girl, and it looked like she wished she'd never asked. As the rest of the posse gathered around them, they began to look a little frightened. They were made to feel even worse when Alex then said, 'Don't be nervous . . .' and stepped towards them.

He didn't seem to notice and continued his sales patter. 'I can draw the pass-out stamp on your arm for £25 each. It's how we've all got in. Come, show me your money.'

Straight away the two girls seemed to hold on to their shoulder bags even tighter than they had already been doing. He moved another pace towards them as the others – Duane, Carlton and myself apart – stood in a line in front of the pair who had their backs to the side of the path.

Fearing the worst, I wanted to say something to try to help them, but I waited to see what would happen first.

'You want to try it?' he continued, doing his best to charm the girls but instead worrying them even more with a leery smile and dirty chuckle.

'How do we know it will work?' said the Lancashire girl's friend. 'What if we pay you and we don't get in?'

'Come back to us here, and I'll give you a refund.'

As the girls both shook their heads, I managed to control a laugh. As if, I thought to myself. I looked sideways at Carlton. He caught me glancing at him but chose to stay focused on his leader and the two girls.

'Got to go down with them,' I whispered to him. 'Get the money once they're in.'

Carlton continued to blank me.

'No way,' said the Lancashire lass.

As Alex took another step towards them, they cringed a bit more, and I still held my breath. Just then, like the cavalry riding over the hill, the lights of a van suddenly illuminated the lane as it came along the road towards us. We were lit up like the proverbial rabbit caught in the headlights. It was something the lot who'd captured me didn't like. They froze momentarily before stepping back into the side of the path and out of the beam of the headlights, the two girls taking their chance and rapidly walking away. I took a step back from where Alex was and turned to try to disappear into the darkness, but before I could go any further a hand grabbed my collar, and I felt a rush of air as Carlton swung the bat with his right hand, again just missing my face.

'Where ya goin', white boy?' Alex said mockingly, laughing at my futile attempt to escape.

With that, and another near miss as the bat again flew inches past my head, we all walked on down the lane for another fifty yards. Another group of people approached as we stood in a clearing at the side of the lane, which was illuminated by the lights from the security fence. There were four of them – two guys and two girls – and again, after they were offered Es or a wrap of charlie, one asked about getting in.

'Thirty pounds each, but I'll get you all in for one hundred,' said Alex.

He was catching on fast. This time, when they asked, he said he'd send two of his soldiers with them to collect the money once they were through. After a few moments' discussion they agreed but sensibly decided that two would try it first.

'The game's up,' I thought to myself, as I watched the first couple get stamped and walk away down the lane with two of the young crew there to make sure they weren't going to get a freebie. The rest of us, including the couple's friends, waited where we were.

Within five or six minutes they were back, one of the youngsters half quizzically, half excitedly, telling his boss that hadn't worked. The two who had been down to the gate shook their heads at their companions as Alex looked at me. He turned to Carlton, who pushed me forward towards Alex with a sharp prod of his bat in my back.

'Why ain't it working?' he demanded, the four customers now looking decidedly nervous as he stood about a yard away square on to me.

I stayed silent.

'Why ain't it working?' he repeated, his tone sounding a little more impatient.

'You ain't doing it right,' I replied quietly.

In reality, of course, I didn't know why it wasn't working either, but I'd said it now and awaited his response. His eyes narrowed, and he came a little closer to me.

'How d'ya mean, I ain't doing it right?'

I looked him in the eyes.

'Once you've drawn it on, you're meant to smudge it and say, "Have a nice time."'

He looked me straight on and, maintaining eye contact, turned his head slightly to one side. It was as though I'd hit him a hammer blow. The key to this scam was a bit of blag, a bit of luck and a lot of good karma – but the nearest he'd come to that was probably korma of the chicken variety, ordered from a takeaway in whatever inner-city ghetto he came from after an evening making shit-loads of money either selling Es and charlie to the local residents or just plain terrorising them. For him, trying to be nice to a complete stranger was going to be a tall order. He turned to the four who had asked about getting in.

'Come,' he said, 'I'll do it again.'

'No thanks,' said one of the girls. 'We'll leave it.'

I was gutted. If they had met me without my new acquaintances, they would have been in by now with no trouble and no questions asked, and I'd have been a few bob richer.

'It will work,' I said, my boldness seemingly surprising Alex and his band of merry men.

'I don't think we can be bothered to try again,' said one of the guys. 'Anyway, they'll remember us at the gate.'

'Trust me, they won't,' I retorted. 'I've been working this for a couple of days.'

I looked at Alex.

'We'll do it for £90,' I said, risking his wrath.

He turned his head a little as if in acceptance, as did the four punters.

'Stamp them up again on the other arm this time,' I said, offering him some advice, 'and don't forget to smudge it.'

He looked at me somewhat awkwardly as the first couple offered him their other arms and waited. He drew the circles, smudged them and, remembering what I'd said, he managed, albeit with the utmost difficulty and in the most quiet of voices to say, 'Have a nice time.'

As he uttered the words, it was as though a part of him died, and once he'd heard himself say it he seemed to pause momentarily as if to reflect on this new persona that dictated he'd have to try to, well, just try to be nice.

Even though I had, ever since my capture, been a second away from a smashed skull, this particular moment almost made me laugh I thought it was so funny – the guy struggling with the concept with which he was now faced. He looked at me, then at the pen he was holding and then said, 'You do it,' and handed me the tool.

Although I was a long way from escaping these guys, I felt that I had gained a small victory over them by taking control of the situation. In my mind I'd decided that I was now engaged in a war of attrition with my captors, and this was definitely a battle won, even if it was of the psychological variety.

The other two punters stepped towards me. As I stamped them, I gave them a real hearty 'Have a nice time,' as if to underline the importance of doing so to Alex. I glanced at him as he looked back with an air of suspicion mixed with disbelief. Meanwhile his mates watched, pondering whether they would, in fact, get their chance to do me over, as it now appeared I was going to be crucial to the operation if they were going to keep doing the stamp.

'Shall I go down with them?' I asked.

Instead of saying anything, Alex nodded a yes before turning to Carlton and Duane.

'You go with them, £90, one at the back and one at the front.'

As I turned away, he held out his hand and said, 'Pen.' I took it out of my pocket and handed it back.

With my two minders in tow, the four newcomers and I set off down the lane, Carlton and Duane walking on either side of me. As we approached the gate and joined the line, Carlton moved in front of me, the four punters following us with Duane behind.

As ever, I repeated whispered instructions to our customers and showed them what I would do when a steward asked to inspect my stamp, and, as I knew it would, it worked a treat, and the four walked through without being challenged. As we approached the end of the barriers, Carlton stopped, turned around and put his arms on either side, blocking the way.

'Money – £90,' he growled, looking at the first guy.

Just as I felt Duane brush by me to watch proceedings and thought this might be another chance to get away, he stopped, put his arm around my shoulder as if in friendship, but, as it came around my neck, I caught sight of the blade in his hand and felt the steel as he pressed it, flat-side on, against my Adam's apple. He gave me a glance, didn't need to say anything. I acknowledged his presence with a resigned blink and watched as the now delighted punters handed over their money to Carlton. As they walked off into the festival, the three of us waited to one side for a few moments before turning and joining the exit queue.

When we returned to the others, we found them trying to hustle some more punters. They didn't seem to be getting any-where. There were five young white guys all aged about seventeen standing in the middle of the path with their way blocked by the blacks. It seemed like they were going to come on heavy, and the young kids were petrified.

'They ain't having it,' Alex said, looking at me as Duane went over to improve his side's chances of an easy turnover.

Sensing an opportunity, I stepped forward between the two groups and addressed the youngsters.

'You want in, lads?' I said, hoping I sounded encouraging.

Although they seemed surprised there was a white face in this crew they were facing, my presence did something to relieve what was a tense situation, and they relaxed a little as the youths opposite stood down, their leader looking on.

'What price did they say?' I asked.

'One hundred and fifty for all of us,' said one with a Yorkshire accent, 'but we're not sure.'

Typical, I thought, a tight-arsed northerner who is, even at £30, getting a bargain, but he still wants to beat the price down. Forgetting my prejudice – it was simply related to the ingrained fact that I hated Leeds United – I turned to Alex, shrugged and said, 'One two five . . . £25 a head?'

He closed his eyes slowly as he swallowed hard. With the faintest movement of his head, he gave his assent and, without speaking, held out his hand and offered me the pen. I went into work mode and proceeded to go through the well-practised routine of getting them in.

Another of Alex's crew called Darnell came along with us this time. At first I thought he was part of the security side of things, but, after he'd been chatting to the five kids all the way down to the gate, and after they'd got in, I saw him pass over a few pills and a couple of wraps, the newcomers happily exchanging them for some £40 or £50. Having returned to Alex, after Darnell and Duane gave him the money they'd collected, he summoned me over. With his hand on my shoulder, Alex walked me a few paces away from everyone else.

Quietly, he said, 'Why ain't it working?'

Why ain't it working? I thought. The fact was they were black, mobbed-up, bullies and horrible. The sad truth was that people like this lot gave other black people a bad name. If anyone saw a crew like the one I'd got mixed up with at a place like a festival, especially this one, or anywhere for that matter, they would instinctively know they were trouble.

A lot of people at Glastonbury weren't streetwise and fell victim to those who, because they had the numbers and could get away with it, were selling rubbish hash and weed, fake substances or simply giving bad deals. It wasn't them being black and standing out more, it was because once you'd handed your money over and found you weren't happy there was no getting it back.

Those who tried were threatened with a serious slap, which was enough to put most people off, and if they didn't heed the warning the tools came out on show, which usually did the trick. Now that there were pills and powder involved, and those selling these drugs didn't mess about when they were solving their problems, the situation had become even worse.

Some were making money mugging people late at night on the paths and lanes that surrounded the festival perimeter, while others were brazen enough to do it on the inside. Considering that in most areas of the festival there was a moral majority of do-gooders, such a crime was high risk for the perpetrator, but, even so, it still went on.

There were two or three cases of gangs steaming crowds watching the bands. Gangs of twenty or thirty would literally barge their way through the throng, flashing knives and demanding money and jewellery, taking it quickly as people hurriedly gave them a £10 or £20 note, chains or bracelets, then continuing to batter their way through.

In London this had been quite a common occurrence at gatherings like the Notting Hill Carnival, and it had even progressed to the London Underground system, but at Glastonbury it was a relatively new phenomenon. I actually saw it happen once, the steamers happy enough if they got a constant flow of folding with no one getting slashed or shanked. Luckily for me I was just to one side, saw it coming and moved further away but was still close enough to be amazed at their brashness. In a crowd of tens of thousands, with no security staff to deal with any trouble, the rampaging mob knew they were on to a sure-fire winner.

The steaming took place along with a lot of other stuff, and the police on the outside and the stewards and organisers on the inside had, over recent years, seen the problem of black gangs out to make money increasing, their attendance coinciding with a dramatic rise in the crime figures for Class-A drugs, violent offences and theft.

'Why ain't it working?' Alex asked again.

I looked deep into his eyes.

'You scare people.'

CHAPTER NINE

Alex called Carlton and two of the younger lot over. After some hushed words, Carlton and one of the others scuttled away, while the rest of his crew and me moved back down the lane towards Gate 3. Within a few minutes we met Carlton and the other guy Alex had despatched coming from the opposite direction. This time they were with another six or seven of their mates. Seemingly knowing the sketch, they stopped, waited for us to draw level and turned to walk with us, forming a loose protective circle around me, thereby spoiling any chance I might have of getting away.

In the light spilling over from the security fence, I saw the features of one of the new arrivals. It was the same person who had tried to sit between Billy and me in the café earlier when we'd gone for something to eat. He saw me glancing at him and, half laughing, gave me a knowing look. We both knew that we'd made each other. I checked the lot who'd just turned up and recognised another one who'd been hanging around with the same guy.

As we went, I could remember exactly that moment when I looked at him to say he'd have to sit somewhere else. I had thought then that it wasn't quite right, but at the time but I couldn't quite see why. It was as clear as anything now. Sitting and eating at the café and staring at the mass of people passing by, my eyes had met those of a couple of black geezers who were with four others. They were just standing there on the other side of the drag, across from where Billy and I were sitting. Looking back, there was more to it, so maybe Alex wasn't lying when he said he'd been watching us.

Even though I had only been in his presence for a couple of hours, I'd made my mind up about Alex. He was the kind of person I'd always hated. It was clear that he loved people giving him respect, and he had a certain swagger that gave me the feeling that he got a kick out of bullying and scaring others. He seemed to revel in the fact that he had a firm grafting for him, obeying his every command and obviously ready to back him up if it came on top. Although he appeared to crave admiration from those with him, he had a way of talking down to everyone, creating an impression that those he was addressing were hardly worthy of being in his company. From the way he had handled the pistol, it was easy to imagine he was used to carrying weapons and that, for him, such implements were an everyday part of life. My thoughts turned to how many people he'd hurt or intimidated and how many lives he might have ruined. I wondered whether he had a girlfriend or even a wife and, if he did, what kind of relationship they had and how much grief he gave her. I bet his mother would be ashamed of him if she could see him now, I thought. To me, he exuded evil.

I thought of Billy, wondered where he was, desperately hoping that the crew holding me captive would run into him and a few of the boys. All the lot I'd previously been to Glastonbury with were here somewhere or other but, unfortunately, nowhere close at hand.

I remembered a night out on the town, a stag night, with Gerry, Keyo, Billy and the rest when, as we came out of a club, we'd run into a gang of lads on holiday. I don't know what the kick-off was about, but I watched Gerry lead the charge, around twenty of us into at least thirty or thirty-five of them, and all our lot came out on top. They'd seen knives and guns aplenty during their time in and around Liverpool, Manchester and Glasgow, and around and about here, there and everywhere in Britain and beyond, and they'd probably quite fancy their chances against the mob that had mugged me.

Thinking again of Billy, I convinced myself that this lot couldn't have got a hold of him because, if they had, they would have been more clued up about the stamp, and they would also probably have mentioned it somewhere down the line.

We walked on and past Gate 3, along the lane in the direction of Gate 2, against the flow of the majority of people, many of them just arriving. With Darnell, Duane and Carlton having been joined by another three in minding me, the rest – Alex apart – set to and began to ply their trade.

'Es? Sweet luv, bruv,' said one to a guy with a girl on his arm, the couple ignoring the offer, but, within moments, the fish were biting and the wraps and pills began to go the way of the customer as four young guys acknowledged a pitch. They stopped, and, after a brief conversation with the vendor, and seemingly well satisfied with the deal, carried on towards the festival entrance.

A second or so later someone else who'd witnessed the transaction and made an enquiry was served up, and Alex's crew were up and running, always working away from where we were but close enough to know that Alex and my minders could bail them out if needed. At the rate they were going, it didn't look like the sellers would need the assistance of Duane, Carlton and all, and I was no nearer to getting away.

'What's your name, boy?'

I turned to face Alex.

'Your name?' he repeated.

'Joe.'

He looked at me as if he was considering my fate, but then his attention was drawn by one of the younger lot who, as he approached, gave him an *I need a word, boss* look, Alex stepping away from me and going over to him. Not thinking about it, I took half a pace backwards, only to feel and hear the rush of air as the bat came swinging across the top of my head, missing my scalp by a couple of inches. When I heard the smack of the end of it hitting his gloved palm, I turned to Carlton, put my hands forward and shrugged my shoulders as if to say, *What was that for?*

The look in his eye told me that he was itching to show his prowess and smash the bat on to my head, but, before I could take an involuntary step away, Alex cut in.

'Joe,' he said, although checking he'd remembered my name correctly, 'it's your lucky day.'

Giving Carlton a glance that said, *Save the bat for when it's needed*, he walked over to me, put his arm around my shoulders and ushered me away from the rest of his posse.

'Wanna know why?' he said, putting his face close to the back of my head, his mouth near my ear. 'You're working for me. From right now,' he continued, 'this is the way things are. You gonna do dat ting, I'm gonna tell you how much, you gonna take the money, you gonna bring it back to me. The only people you gonna speak to are the people I say you gonna speak to. D'ya get me?' He looked past me to where Duane, Carlton and my other minders were, and, with a confident, almost smug, expression, he looked back at me and repeated, 'D'ya get me?'

Feeling the stares of those behind me, I closed my eyes and nodded slightly. Encouraging me to go with him by way of a push, we walked over to where the younger lot were talking to a group of six who wanted to get into the festival, and he looked at the two from his lot who seemed to be doing the negotiating. Motioning them to step away, Alex spoke to one of those who wanted a stamp.

'This is Joe,' he said. 'He will sort you out and make sure you get in.'

He gave me the pen, and I went through the motions of stamping them up, explaining how it worked as I went, while Alex had a few hushed words with the one I'd marked first. Their conversation over, Alex turned to walk past me, and, as he did, he whispered, 'One fifty, everyone.'

'Come on then, let's go,' I said, leading the way and causing Duane and those assigned to take care of me to move quickly to make sure I wasn't trying anything funny. I could see their presence was making the six uncomfortable, and I turned to one of them and, putting on what I hoped was a reassuring smile, said, 'It's OK, they're just here to look after us.'

As the punter smiled back, I felt a prod of the baseball bat in my lower back as Carlton let me know that he and his mates were still with me. I turned back to the customer, but he was speaking to the girl on his left and hadn't seen the 'keep quiet' reminder I'd just been given. I continued walking, my peripheral vision left and right making out two black faces walking parallel with me either side, and, as we entered the queue to get in, I had two in front and one in extremely close attendance behind me.

Not wishing to risk what probably would have been nothing less than a slash across my back with a blade or the bat on my head, I did as I had been instructed, stayed calm and carried on with the business of getting the customers through the gate.

Within ten minutes the six were in, I'd collected the money and, without a word being exchanged between Carlton, Duane and the others, we'd returned to where Alex was waiting. He took me to one side and turned his back on everyone else. He said nothing but rubbed his thumb against the first two fingers of his right hand. As I reached to get the cash out of my pocket, he pointed at me.

'Shhhh,' he whispered, causing me to cup my hand around the wad of notes before I handed them over.

'How much?' he whispered under his breath.

'One fifty,' I replied quietly. 'What you said.'

Glancing at the money in his hand, he squeezed the folded notes as if checking the amount I had said was correct and slipped the wad into his front pocket. Saying nothing, he put his arm on my shoulder and gently turned me in the direction of everyone else at which Carlton, Duane and three of the others re-formed their protective circle, and we moved off, this time up the lane away from Gate 3 and towards Gate 2.

Like Alex, Duane and Carlton seemed to thrive on acting tough, and both gave off an air of evil. They, too, seemed to love the fact that they could snap their fingers and people would go running for them. I wondered how many they had cut or battered on their way up the ladder. Their spiteful and malevolent attitude towards me and those I'd seen them do business with was sickening. I was sure they thought that the way they went about things was the norm, that scaring and bullying people was the way to gain respect. I wondered about the younger guys tagging along in the crew, who all seemed to look up to Alex, Carlton and Duane. They were role models for these young acolytes who would, no doubt, want to emulate their heroes and, at some stage, probably go on to commit acts of violence – if they hadn't done so already – in order to prove their worth to both those they followed and their contemporaries. All in all, it was a nasty crew that I'd got mixed up with.

It took us ages to get around to Gate 2, due to the fact that they were selling their gear and had also picked up a few new punters who I'd had to get in. Gate 3 was still nearer, meaning a walk back for me and my minders every time we had to escort a customer in.

It was the same procedure every time with Alex's E-sellers and scouts touting the stamp and me doing my bit getting them in and collecting the fee. Anyone in a group of four or more was being charged £25 per head while ones, twos and threes were paying £30, and they were coughing up with no question, happy they would be saving a good wedge off the real cost of a ticket, the majority of the balance going towards the purchase of their weekend's drug requirements.

By the time we got to Gate 2, it must have been around 1.30am, but there were still quite a few people hanging around. I was quickly called into action again and took another thirteen or fourteen in. I'd lost track of the total but kept count of the money I'd handed over to Alex since my capture, and so far it was £1,140.

For some reason he didn't like £5 notes, and when I gave them to him as part of the entrance fee he sneered and handed them back. So far I'd been given £40, but that was like losing a £50 note and finding a penny. Business was booming, and I was missing out, my hard graft making someone else rich while I was getting colder, feeling hungry and becoming more tired by the minute. I was gutted.

After a while the lanes at the crossing by Gate 2 became empty, as the majority of the festival slept or danced the night away at one of the raves in the camping fields or at the stalls on the drags such as Joe Bananas. I could hear the music booming away in the distance, but where we were it was dead apart from the odd person leaving the festival looking slightly the worse for wear.

We began to walk back along the lane towards Gate 3. By this time there were about twenty in Alex's crew, and what with the scouts leading at the front, the whole group must have been spread along a distance of some fifty yards. After five minutes, in the distance to our right and made visible by the light coming from inside the festival, we saw six or seven travellers obviously looking for a way into the festival. There were various weak spots in the Glastonbury defences where, in some places, holes under the fence reappeared with annual regularity, and these guys looked like they were preparing to go through one.

The travellers had, for years, been used to getting free access to Glastonbury, but, after recent problems with the security stewards and the police, their presence was no longer welcome. However, they were experts in the art of festivals and knew Glastonbury well, and there was no way that they were going to pay to get in.

One of Alex's soldiers came rapidly towards him and whispered something in his ear. After instructing three of his lads to go to investigate, Alex led the rest of us a short distance back the way we'd come to await developments. I watched as they approached the group trying to get in, and, as I turned my head away to look to the front, I wondered what kind of conversation these two groups could possibly have.

In previous years, it was the travellers who, on the whole, were regarded as the main suppliers of substances such as acid and speed, but now, with the penchant for the majority of those who chose to partake being Es and cocaine, the past couple of Glastonbury Festivals had seen the blacks take over the market. As well as that, they also now seemed to be controlling many of the main selling areas in the lanes and by the entrance gates. The travellers hated them.

Walking in single file, I was seven or eight people behind Alex. We'd gone about a hundred yards when the sound of raised voices and someone whistling a shrill warning signal cut through the night. Alex turned, as did those who had been in front of me, and they were now walking back past me towards the sound of the whistle and what sounded like a serious disagreement. The shouting was momentarily drowned out by the revs from the engine of a motor vehicle coming along the lane, but then there was a sudden increase in the volume of the voices followed by another whistle, this time sounded twice.

Whether they forgot me unintentionally, or it was just a case of them putting riding to the rescue of their mates ahead of their guard duty, I'll never know, but as soon as they heard that second whistle those meant to be minding me and the rest of those with them were on their way, half walking, half running, towards what was obviously a dispute involving the travellers.

As the lights of what I could now see was a van illuminated the lane, the shape of Alex and his mates came into focus for a split second, their bodies dodging into the side of the lane to get past the oncoming vehicle and on to the scene of the action.

I stepped to the side of the lane and caught sight of Darnell, Carlton, Duane and their section not too far behind the others but also standing aside to let the van go by. They were now at least thirty yards along the lane from me, and once the van had passed they started running towards the travellers. It was the furthest from me that any of them had been since my capture, and I knew this was when I was going to get away.

As the van drew level with me, I let it pass before running behind it and, grabbing the back-door handle, pulled myself up and on to the back footplate, clinging on as I felt myself being carried further and further away from Alex, his crew and their horrible, evil world.

Although it was dark, because there weren't too many people about, the driver was able to put on a spurt here and there, and, after no more than a couple of minutes, I was back at the cross-roads for the Gate 2 entrance. As the van slowed to turn to the right, I jumped off.

I watched the van drive off in the direction of the main road that led to the nearby village of Pilton until its rear lights disappeared, listened to the sound of the engine fading as it got further away. For a moment I wondered whether I should have stayed on the back and let it carry me away from the festival, but the chance to take that option had now gone.

As I stood there alone in the night, I reflected on how lucky I'd been to come to no harm and get away in one piece after all that had happened to me in the last few hours. I was confident in as much as Alex and his troops were at least fifteen minutes' marching distance away, and I knew I had a bit of that time to think about my next move.

Basically, I had two choices. One was to leave the festival and head home; the other to stay on and risk running into Alex's crew again. After some contemplation, I decided to stay and began walking down the slope and through the entrance of Gate 2, continuing down the track that was Muddy Lane into the festival area past a field full of tents to my right. Spotting the remnants of a camp fire and no one around it, I diverted away from the path and sat there, my back to the field and my vision on the lane.

Warmed by the embers of the fire, and in the light of their glow, I took my boots off, pulled up my socks and generally adjusted my clothing. Feeling the money-belt, my heart skipped when I thought about how gutted I'd have been if this had been found by my attackers. I didn't bother to open it but instead just ensured that the clasp was pulled tight and secure before tucking my T-shirt over it and leaving my 'festival' Ben Sherman shirt untucked. As I stood to fasten my jacket, my hand brushed along my chest, and I felt an object in my inside pocket. It was a ten-pack of Benson and Hedges along with skins, lighter and a little lump of hash which, surprisingly, Alex and his boys hadn't confiscated. I hadn't even thought about a joint since I'd been captured, but I certainly felt like having one now.

I built a spliff and, for a few seconds, enjoyed the taste of the hash and the tranquillity of the night. Then, and it was probably the smoke, an overwhelming sense of wanting to get back to where I'd camped with Billy and Gruff and his lot came over me. Although I wasn't sure where Alex and his mob were based, I was certain I didn't want to risk running into them again.

So far, I'd only seen them on the lanes, but, thinking about what Alex had said about watching me, I thought there would be a good chance that they'd be plotted up somewhere around the entrance into Gate 3 in one of the fields on the outside. With that in mind, I decided to make my way further into the festival and up towards the Green Fields. There were definitely more people up and about on the inside than there were on the out, which was good for me in one way but bad in another.

The fact that it was more crowded meant that if Alex and his boys did decide to try to find me, they'd have a hard job, as my form would simply merge in with everyone else, and I'd be harder to spot. But against that, if they were also on the inside, they, too, would be able to melt into the crowds and make it harder for me to spot them.

Joe Bananas was still on, the DJ keeping the ravers, most of who had obviously swallowed an E, happy, and as I passed by I stopped to buy myself a couple of blankets. I say blankets, but they were just old unusable electric blankets, and either child or single-bed size at that. They all had the electric leads sticking out of them, and in some cases the switch and the plug were still attached. I bought two, one to put around my shoulders and one for my head, which must have made me look like I was wearing a pink sari or a shawl. I didn't care, though. There were loads of people here who looked a lot weirder than I did. I was warm and, although somewhat conspicuous, in a form of a disguise. Things like fashion responsibility or even looking half-decent didn't come into it.

Walking up the drag in the direction of the Stones, I kept the blanket pulled over my head to avoid being spotted, although the closer I got to the Green Fields the less I felt paranoid about being seen by Alex and his lot. By the time I was halfway along the drag, the blankets were off, the walk having warmed me up, and I veered off the path and found a small marquee that during the day was a café. It had now closed for business, but inside it had a few squatters who'd decided to make the place their bedroom for the night. I found an empty bit of the floor away from the entrance and, using one of the blankets as a mattress, wrapped the other around my shoulders, curled up and dozed for a time then eventually fell asleep.

It was daylight when I opened my eyes. I could feel the heat of the sun beating down outside, as I stared through the entrance of the tent. A few feet from where I was, someone else who'd also crashed out in the café was lying asleep, and the watch on his arm told me it was 6.30am. The temperature inside the café had risen a few degrees since I'd gone to sleep, and I could feel the sweat beginning to break on my forehead. I was thirsty, but there was no one behind the counter, so a drink would have to wait, at least until I found a stall or a café that was open.

A sudden flashback to the previous night focused my mind, and I decided to get back to my camp and safety as quickly as I could. Instead of going down what would have been my usual route, I avoided the main drag and headed straight around the back of the Circus Tent, which was to the left of where I was now facing, and directly towards Gate 3.

Being doubly careful that I wasn't spotted, I reached my encampment in about twenty minutes. It was quiet and peaceful, with very few people up and about. Gruff and H had shut their van up like they always did when they crashed out in the back of it, and it was the same for the others. The flap to Billy's tent was about a third of the way open, and, peering in, I could see him lying asleep.

Not bothering to wake anyone, I started getting washed, freshened up and changed and prepared myself for the coming day. Finding a small backpack I had among my kit, I packed two shirts, two caps and a windcheater as well as the usual bag with my toothbrush, toothpaste and gear for keeping clean. I won't be caught today, I thought, as I looked at the bag which now contained two disguises. I felt the money-belt around my waist and took out the £300, went to the wheel of the van where, the night before, I had put the money I'd made that evening and placed the two lots of notes together. Thinking about getting mugged again made me wary, and, just in case I didn't make it back before everyone got off on Monday, I didn't want Gruff driving the van away with no knowledge of the cash I'd stashed.

I couldn't get into the van without waking Gruff and H, so I thought I'd take a chance and leave my money in a bag inside my tent. I still had the £40 Alex had allowed me to keep, so I decided I'd just go out with that and leave the rest of the cash in the safety of our camp. The wad of £900 and the £1,300 that H was looking after made £2,200 and, all in all, despite what had happened to me, it was still a good result. Even if I didn't see Gruff and H before they left the festival, I knew for a fact that they would take my tent and the rest of my kit back to their place in Dorset. As I had left my car there, I'd have to go to collect it anyway, so that made perfect sense.

It was now 7.15am on what was another beautiful morning, and I was ready for the rest of the day. All I needed to do now was get something to eat, have a spliff and crash for an hour or so until about ten or eleven and then get to work. Just as I was about to put the wad of money away, I felt my heart drop as I suddenly realised that I didn't have an ultraviolet pen.

'Shhhiiittt!' I spat out, my heart skipping again. Alex's lot still had the pen. Instinctively, I began to feel my pockets to try to find it but stopped as soon as I started. I didn't have it, they did. Billy, I thought, and, with a rush of relief, I went to his tent. Unzipping the flap quietly, I entered and gently shook him.

'Billy.'

No movement.

'Billy,' I repeated but with a little more urgency and volume as I shook him harder.

Moving slightly but still asleep, he exhaled a deep breath and turned away from me.

I tried again. 'Billy,' I hissed. 'Give us your pen.'

His head turned, and he sighed, wakened slightly and said hoarsely, 'Lost it . . .'

'What?'

'Lost it. Where's yours?' he whispered as he turned over and went back to sleep.

Biting hard so I didn't let the involuntary rage welling up inside me spill out, I stepped from Billy's tent and aimed a kick at a bottle of water, which went flying past the van and into the hedge. I was fuming, the anger causing my legs to go weak at the knees. I felt like going back into Billy's tent and booting him in the head. Lost it? How could he have been so stupid? At least I had legitimate reasons for not having mine, but what excuse did he have? I was seething.

Billy was a brilliantly talented guitarist, and he could also write a decent song, but personal circumstances put paid to him having a normal life, and he descended into the drudgery of the then pre-valent Scottish inner-city chemical drug scene and, at home in Glasgow, his life was a mess. He had come down south to England to try to kick his heroin habit and ended up in the company of Gerry, Keyo and Sparky in the town in Devon where we lived. That is how I had met Billy.

I had an interest in making music, and the first time I heard him play a guitar I knew I had to try to do something with Billy. We spent a lot of time writing songs and recording demos at home, and for the four or five years we'd been knocking about together he'd lodged with me at the two houses I had going. We knew each other well and regularly, often quite badly, got on each others nerves.

A couple of months prior to the festival, I wasn't in a particu-larly good mood when it came to us having to move out of my house in Dorset. I was broken-hearted at leaving and on the last morning was rushing around the place doing the remaining packing and sorting out what we were taking while Billy was being a proper nuisance, sitting there not helping. Something was said, and after a few moments of arguing we began fighting.

On that occasion he'd come off worst, having suffered a broken hand after punching me. That bit of our fight must have looked comical. We were doing our best to kill each other with months of pent-up tension spilling out when, after aiming a swing at me and connecting with the back of my head, Billy screamed with pain, shouting, 'I've hurt my hand.'

Hostilities immediately ceased, the argument forgotten as we both inspected the hand, which had started to swell up rapidly. I finished packing my van with our gear, and within an hour he was at the accident and emergency department of the local hospital.

After treatment, he was discharged with a plaster of Paris cast on his hand, and we were off, heading west towards Devon, leaving Dorset behind us and laughing about what had happened.

As suddenly as my rage about him not having his pen had come on, it went away. OK, so I was distraught at having lost mine to Alex, and Billy had probably lost his when he'd been off his face somewhere, but having an argument with him about the pen was the last thing I needed. Then the anger started welling up again when I thought of all the people I should be getting in to the festival, the money I would be missing out on because I didn't have the tools the trade required. Even though I'd already made what for me was a small fortune, I didn't want to stop. My money head was working in 4/4 time, and I wanted more.

Within a second I made my mind up that I'd go to the nearest stationer's or hardware shop and buy a couple of new pens. Feeling the wad of notes that I was still holding, I unwrapped £50 and put the rest away and stashed it inside a holdall with a few of my clothes, something that would definitely not be left behind if one of the others had to pack up for me.

Once I had left everything in my tent just as I wanted it, I zipped up the flap and sat outside, rolled a couple of joints, smoking the first as I made the second and broke about a sixteenth off of my lump of hash, all the while thinking about the job of trying to get myself some more ultraviolet pens.

I knew it would take ages to get anywhere away from the festival site, especially at this time of the morning when the likelihood of hitching a lift was nil. The commercial vehicles were not stopping for anyone, and the majority of what traffic there was on the road would be inbound. I would have to start walking.

Finishing the smoke, I rechecked my backpack, and, satisfied I had everything I needed for the day, I set off on foot away from the festival and along the lanes in the direction of Shepton Mallet, the home of the world-renowned Bath And West Showground, a distance of about three miles. The further from the festival I got, the more confident I was that I wouldn't cross the path of Alex and his crew, and I walked in the middle of the lanes, hurrying to reach the nearest town but at the same time enjoying the solitude and quiet of a lovely summer's morning deep in the countryside.

In parts, the twisting road was lined on either side by trees, which, compared with the stretches that were exposed to the sunlight, were darker and cooler and a touch mysterious, the chill in the air making my spine tingle and giving me a greater sense of urgency.

After twelve minutes I came across a stall selling teas, coffees and sandwiches at the side of the lane. Ordering a coffee, a roll and a Mars Bar, I sat there for fifteen minutes, resting and eating my breakfast before continuing. Soon I reached the A37 road to Shepton Mallet, and after another forty minutes or so of walking I reached its outskirts.

It was just on 9am, and the sleepy town was seeing the first local shoppers venturing out of their houses to buy newspapers, milk and other such provisions. I found an ironmonger's and asked if they stocked ultraviolet security markers. They didn't and neither did they know of any place that did. Wells was the next nearest biggest town, so I waited for a bus that would take me there.

After arriving in Wells and not having any joy finding the required implement, I was advised to try Bristol, and by midday I had arrived in the centre of the city, where it wasn't long before I found a shop selling office supplies and the like.

'Hi,' I said, as I approached the counter, directing my greeting to the woman standing behind it. 'Do you sell ultraviolet security markers?'

Her eyes narrowed. 'We do. They're over there.'

I went to the shelf she'd pointed at and saw three. Picking them all up, I took them back to the counter and handed over a £20 note.

Handing me my change, she gave me a quizzical look and said, 'Can you tell me what's going on?'

'How do you mean?' I replied innocently.

'Well, ever since yesterday, there's been a constant stream of people coming in and buying this type of marker,' she said, glancing over to the now empty space on the shelf, 'and you've just bought the last three.'

'I haven't got a clue,' I replied, looking at the spot she'd focused on before I thanked her and made my way out of the shop and back on to the busy street.

Of course, I did have a clue. I knew exactly what had happened. Loads of people who had been getting to the festival without tickets and expecting to have to go under or over the fence had gained entry via the stamp, either courtesy of me and Billy or one of the many others who had now begun to work it. As soon as they were inside, they must have called their mates at home, told them the coup and got them on it, inspiring a sudden upsurge in entrepreneurial ingenuity that Maggie Thatcher herself would have appreciated.

It didn't matter. It was done now. As long as I made my share, it didn't bother me knowing others were either stamping themselves up and getting their mates in or coining it as they went into business themselves. As I made my way along the street towards the main bus station, all I knew was that I didn't want to get captured again and that, once I reached Glastonbury, the competition would be fierce.

CHAPTER TEN

The previous year's Glastonbury Festival was the first where I had made money. In 1992 I went with Gruff and H and a few of their friends, and their style of doing things was a lot quieter than that of the usual crew. Gruff and H, childhood sweethearts and married for years, liked the sensible life and went to Glastonbury to watch particular bands or listen to or watch other performing artists. Camping with them was pleasant, organised and peaceful, and, although Gruff and H had the occasional drag of a spliff, they were happy with a few drinks and something nice to eat. Everyone had their own place to kip, and their kit was in their own particular space.

On the other hand, staying with my crew was hectic. The Scottish contingent – namely Keyo, Gerry and Sparky – a few Scousers including Tony, some Brummies, Mancs and myself had, after the first time we attended together, returned home like prophets, spreading the word about the laugh we'd had and how we were going again the following year. The Glastonbury Festival soon became not only a part of our lives but also the stuff of legend. By the time the ritual had been established, the routine was the same every year. We, the prophets, would set out early like an advance guard, establish our own bridgehead, and, when our base had been set up, reinforcements from various parts of the country would make their way there to join us and to resupply us with the copious amounts of cannabis and alcohol we'd battered making our assault.

All this activity ensured that, back in our adopted hometown, the jungle drums were beating. People were walking into one or two of the main pubs say, on the Thursday or Friday night, asking where a particular person might be and, on being told that he or she had gone to Glastonbury, were, literally on the spot, making their minds up to go as well. That meant, for about three or four Glastonbury Festivals in a row, by the time Saturday night came, people ended up crashing five or six to a two-man tent.

A few, who'd been in the pub one minute and found themselves sitting in a car heading towards Somerset the next, came with nothing but a few quid, enough drugs to last them the weekend and just the clothes they were dressed in – not at all prepared for a night and probably the next day and another night at Glastonbury. Nothing was sacred, which meant everybody who'd come from the pub would have to borrow things like soap and towels from those who'd come prepared, as well as dry clothes and waterproof jackets when it rained.

We were all mates and had, during the course of moving to and settling in the same small town, stayed with each other at some point, worked together or generally accepted others on the strength that they knew someone we knew. At Glastonbury it was like being in one big happy family, and we generally mucked in together, but, because we knew each other so well, there were constant arguments about who'd smoked what and whose turn it was to skin up, who'd drunk whose drink, how much someone had already borrowed since they'd been there and the usual assorted banter. All in all it ended up being an extension of what life was like at home . . . but in the middle of a field.

We, the prophets, had a brilliant time when we first went together. Within a couple of hours of arriving we went out and, meeting others we knew along the way, found ourselves in the massive blue marquee that was the Acoustic Tent only a matter of a few minutes' walk away from where we'd decided to set up camp.

One or two had already swallowed their tabs of acid, and, as we snaked our way into the seated area and climbed across the terraced wooden seating, we all managed to squeeze into the same two rows of seats. The band – it might well have been The Saw Doctors – had just come on stage, and within seconds of starting their foot-tapping, knee-slapping, yee-haw-shouting music, the whole place was rocking. Those who were tripping all seemed to start coming up at the same time, and the high they were getting was soon rubbing off on the rest of us. It was brilliant. We were all together and buzzing at getting in, and the beer and cider, let alone the acid and the hash, were kicking in.

Almost hysterical with laughter, we found ourselves being bounced a foot or so upwards then downwards as the wooden terraced seats that we were sitting upon were being shaken violently by the hundreds of people who, like us, were getting right into the music. The thought of the whole structure suddenly collapsing did momentarily cross my mind, but, upon turning to my left and seeing Keyo hanging on to a wooden upright post with tears of laughter streaming down his face, there was nothing for me to do but start laughing myself, and that I did until my sides were aching.

Every year since, I remember that night as soon as I see the Acoustic Tent and always think about the rest of the prophets, but, even with such happy memories in my mind, I was happy, this year at least, to camp with Gruff and his friends.

The advantage was that, knowing where they'd be and if I wanted, I could always go around and call for the prophets at their camp, but if I fancied a different buzz I could have the relative peace and tranquillity of staying away from the madness. I was more than happy dipping in and out and always managed to strike the right balance between the two.

Some of the prophets and their associates used to do a bit of drug-selling, and one or two others did a few things that they kept to themselves, and whatever it was it earned them a few quid, but, as for the rest of us, we were usually happy just getting high on being at the festival.

Ever since my first Glastonbury, I swore that, the next time I went, I'd take some cans of lager or do something to try to earn some money, but, by the time the festival came around, it was either too late or, more usually, I was too skint to get it together. This particular year ran the same course as every other one.

I had more often than not scraped enough money to last me the duration – or so I thought – but, by the time Sunday came, I'd usually borrowed at least £50 to keep me going. In 1992 Gruff and H had decided to stay until the Monday morning, and, by Sunday lunchtime, H was the one who had to bail me out. I had taken the money and arranged to meet Gruff, H and the rest of their contingent for a late drink on the Sunday night. That would leave me a few hours to do my own thing before I'd have to meet them, and I found myself walking up the slow incline towards the Stones.

Reaching the railway line, now defunct but still an important landmark within the festival site, I wandered off to the left towards one of the camping areas near to the Green Field in the hope of catching up with some friends I'd met on the Friday but hadn't seen since.

The weather that weekend had been kind, and the sun was shining, giving everybody at the festival the chance to catch a few rays while chilling out in the afternoon to ready themselves for the finale that would take place later during the hours of darkness. Because of the heat, I had turned off the drag and cut across the field next to the one I was headed for, trying to save myself a few minutes' walk, even though if I'd stayed on the main pathway I was six or seven minutes away. As I made my way through the mass of tents, I was keeping my eyes to the ground so I didn't catch my feet on a tent peg or a guy rope.

Picking my way between two tents, I saw something glistening in the grass. As my vision narrowed and my brain clicked into gear, my heart rate almost doubled as I realised that I'd spotted what looked like a clear plastic bank bag full of someone's kit.

After freezing on the spot momentarily, I moved quickly to my left and stood on the package. I bent down on my right knee, fiddled with the laces of my boot and looked around. I was in a blind spot, and, prior to finding the bag, I was unaware of anyone even walking the path I'd taken let alone following me. I took a sharp breath and, as I raised my foot, reached for the package.

Sure enough, I had found someone else's stash, and the bag containing it was almost bursting it was that tightly packed. Instinctively, I slipped the package down the front of my jeans and looked up. The coast was still clear. Raising myself up slowly, I glanced over the top of the tents in the direction that I was headed and decided to make my way there quickly. It wouldn't be long before the former owner of the contraband realised it was missing and steps would soon be retraced.

I walked slowly at first, but, as well as taking the occasional glance at the path for obstacles, it was my peripheral vision that was working overtime. After a minute or so I was well clear of where I'd found the bag and speeded up. As I got to the gate at the end of the field, I knew that I was as good as in the clear and that I was only moments or so away from where I was going.

Entering my friends' encampment, I let on to a few of the faces, but instead of stopping and chatting I headed for a green Ford Sierra and made my way around to the open driver's door.

'Alright, la?' said Stephen, as he swung his legs out of the car and turned to face me. We shook hands.

'I need a word.'

'Go on . . .'

'I think I might have had a bit of luck, and I just need to sit in the back of the motor a minute and have a look at something.'

Stephen chuckled, nodded, and a second later I was in the car and examining my find.

'No peeping, you,' I said half jokingly, as I saw him try to catch a glance of what I was doing through the rear-view mirror.

'I'm watchin' ya.' came the reply.

I examined the contents of the bag. There were five magazine-paper wraps of something or other, twelve deals – twist-wrapped in cling-film – of a dark-green weed, as though they'd been weighed up as eighths, and four weighed quarters of clean-looking soap bar.

'Whoa!' I said, letting out the breath I'd been holding as I counted up the spoils. 'Is this any good to you?'

I handed Stephen one of the wraps. A second later he winked his approval through the mirror.

'Where d'ya get this then?'

'Ask no questions, tell no lies . . .'

'Go on . . .'

Smiling, I said, 'I'm not telling ya.'

Using the rear-view mirror again, Stephen made sure his eyes caught mine square on. The creases at the corner of his eyes narrowed, and a smile crossed his lips.

'Go on . . .' he repeated.

'What's in the wrap,' I asked, looking away and down, squeezing open one of the remaining four. Licking the end of my little finger, I dipped it into the parcel and made sure that enough had stuck to it to get a flavour, put it on the tip of my tongue. It tasted like cocaine. I began to flick open the others. They all contained the same type of powder.

'Go on . . .' said Stephen for a third time, pausing, and then adding, 'before I fuckin' kill ya, you horrible skinny Chelsea cunt.'

'Charlie, ain't it?' I said, regaining eye contact.

He looked at me – or, rather, right through me. I stared back into the reflection of the mirror and raised my arms.

'Hands up, Stephen, I just found it. Honest.'

Before he could say anything else, I went on to explain that I had made the discovery at a location that was, from where we were currently situated at least, 'miles away', thereby cutting out the possibility that the stash could have, in fact, been dropped by someone Stephen knew.

'Well done, lad.'

'Coca, ain't it?'

His eyes betrayed the smile he was showing. I was glad it was cocaine. Although I had, over the course of the years, the very occasional dabble of speed, it was one of several drugs that I didn't bother with or even really like to handle. A few years back I'd seen some friends of mine become regular intravenous users of speed, and that was enough to put me off for life. The same went for cocaine, although in that particular case, the price it was sold for was enough to put me off as well as an aversion. I was, though, more interested in the lumps of solid hashish and the green. I motioned to the wrap I'd given him.

'That's yours. How much do you think the bag's worth?'

He looked at the wrap.

'There's not a half a gram . . . maybe a quarter . . . if that.'

Lifting the bag closer to his eyes for a closer inspection, he continued, 'They're probably meant to be £20 deals, you know, five quarters to a gram instead of four, and they'd have probably punted them for twenty, maybe twenty-five –'

'Have a look at these,' I cut in. 'They look to me like they're all the same.'

'I'd say so as well,' replied Stephen after he'd inspected them closely.

'Here, have another one,' I said, passing him back one of the wraps that he'd just handed back to me.

'Ta, la!' he smiled.

'Have one of these as well,' I said, handing him one of the quarters of the hash.

'Nice one.'

'What about the rest of it? Do you think anyone around here might fancy buying something off me? Cheap like . . .'

'Ask them.'

With that, and after a few minutes chatting with the rest of those camping with Stephen, I'd sold the three remaining bags of charlie (less a dabble or so for myself) for £25 the lot – cheap, but, considering the circumstances in which the gear came into my possession, I was pleased. After keeping a quarter lump of the soap bar for myself, I got another £25 for the two other quarters that were left. Fifty pounds in my pocket, a nice lump for myself and I still had the twelve or so bags of green. I was happy.

'What do you reckon on that then?' I said to Tommy, one of Stephen's mates.

I passed him a wrap of green. I undid one that was slightly bigger than the rest and which, unlike the others, looked as though it had been opened and rewrapped several times. It was probably the previous owners' personal. I put the package to my nose and Tommy did likewise. It smelled good to me.

'Smells OK,' he came back, 'but you know what they say, don't you?'

'What, that the proof is in the smoking?'

'Yeah, something like that.'

We both reached for Rizla papers and a cigarette each and started to skin up our joints. Within minutes we were both agreed that it was a nice smoke.

'Do you reckon these are twenties or what?' I asked.

'Yeah, probably, although if I was selling them I'd probably ask for fifteens, just to be on the safe side.'

I mentally did the sums and realised that, if I managed to sell the remaining eleven packages at that price, I'd earn myself £165. That would do me. After staying for another half an hour, and leaving enough of the green for the lads to have a couple of joints to share, I said my farewells and headed away, back towards the drag that would lead me down the hill and on in the direction of the busiest part of the festival.

I decided to get back to where Gruff and the others were camped. I wasn't expecting to see them, as they were already out and about, but I wanted to stash both the money I had just collected and the majority of the lump of hash I'd kept for myself before I went about the task of selling the bags of green.

Back at base, I found the keys to the van, opened the back door and sat inside. After rolling a couple of joints of the soap to walk around with, I cut about an eighth off from the lump and, together with the £50 I had just earned, put the rest into a plastic shopping bag and tied it with a knot. Exiting the van and ensuring no one was clocking me, I put the bag under the vehicle next to the several bags of refuse that had accumulated during the course of our camping. Making sure I had everything I needed for the next few hours, I locked up and replaced the keys under the front wheel of the van.

Walking back towards Gate 3, I was happy in as much as I had the money that I owed H and also a nice little bit of puff. It had been a good day. I would be able to leave Glastonbury knowing that, once I'd paid H, I wouldn't owe anyone any money, and the lump of hash would save me the bother of running around trying to get some when I was back home.

Although I was smoking one joint, had another in my pocket with a little lump of the hash, my major worry about either getting nicked by robbers with the money and hash, or even losing it, was put to one side. I wasn't so bothered about the green. I'd try to do it in, but, if it came on top, I'd take the chance, ditch the gear and do my best to get off. I just didn't want to risk letting the money that would pay my debt slip through my fingers or, come to that, lose the lump of soap that was clean, smooth and, so far at least, going down a treat.

Walking down the lane, I saw a couple of hippies who were sitting on one side in a gap in the foliage that divided the path from the fence. As I passed, one of them looked up, and, as our eyes met, he nodded in acknowledgement. I returned the gesture and slowed to a halt.

'How ya doin', mate?'

'Yeah, man, we're fine. How are you?'

'Yeah, I've had a great time. When did you get here?'

'Been here since Friday morning.'

'Nice one. What you up to then?'

'We've lost our pot, and we're waiting for our friend to come back. He's gone to try and score some more.'

'I've got a bit of green I could do you. It's going cheap.'

'Yeah?' said the other hippy, turning his face away in a gesture of indifference.

'Here, mate,' I retorted, 'you can try it first if you want.'

He turned, looked at me and held out his palm. Opening the bag that I'd tried, I handed him enough to roll a joint and took some out for myself. As they sat straight to build up, I sat down alongside them and began to do likewise, and we started to chat about what we'd seen and done over the previous three or four days.

We didn't look out of place at the side of the path. People would literally sit down at the nearest convenient point, and, all along the length of the path, there were groups just like us, chatting and sharing a drink. It was one of the great things about the festival. Complete strangers would strike up conversations, talk happily for a while and then disappear, more often than not never to see each other again.

Even on the outside of the festival, the police only came by occasionally, and, by the time you had spotted them, you'd have time to dib your joint, stash your gear and, as long as you weren't looking too moody, you wouldn't usually warrant a second glance. The stewards and other Glastonbury officials wouldn't even bat an eyelid at the sight of a joint being smoked. You just carried on sitting it out where you were, waiting for the time that the danger had passed and you could relight your joint.

It turned out that the two hippies had not only lost their stash but had also suffered at the hands of a rip-off merchant, who, on taking their money, had left them with a lump of plastic wrapped in silver paper in place of black hash and had charged them £35 for the privilege. That probably explained why the guy had been wary when I said I could sort him out. Taking a long pull on the joint he'd just made, he looked at me, at his friend and again at me and exhaled.

'This is nice, man. How much are you selling it for?'

'Twenty pounds. I could do you two for £35.'

'Can I see the deals?'

'Sure you can, no problem.'

'Thirty-five quid for two, did you say?'

'Go on,' I replied, 'that's what I said. Pick a couple of these.'

I held out half a dozen in my palm, and he took two, gave me the money and that was that. The deal was done, and all parties were happy. Two down and nine to go, and I was off and running.

Over the course of the next couple of hours, having re-entered the festival, I managed to sell another two for £35 the pair and three more at £20 each. After having something to eat and drink, I sat and smoked the joint of hash that I had left from earlier. Totalling up what I'd made, I reckoned it to be £130 less the £10 I'd just spent buying the grub. There was £120 in my pocket, and, with four deals left, even if I did them at £15 each, I could still end the night with £180, less what I would spend later.

I decided to spend the remaining hour or so of sunlight wandering around the Healing and Spiritual Fields, taking in the unique sense of peace, calm and tranquillity that overwhelms everybody who goes to these parts of the festival. One finds oneself transported away from the madness that is the rest of Glastonbury and, considering the amount of time I had spent awake and buzzing over the past few days – scared in case I missed anything that happened – chilling out in the field I was in suited me fine. I found a space at the back of a marquee large enough to lie down in and dropped wearily to the floor. The amount of walking that I'd done during the day had caught up with me, and, as I stretched and yawned, I could feel myself dropping off.

An hour and a half later I awoke, refreshed and glad of the catnap. I got myself together and left the tent. It was now well past sunset, and, as I stepped into the night, the chill in the air that accompanied the darkness was emphasised by the stars gleaming down from clear skies. The Healing Field was deserted, and, when I saw the lights at the end of the field that came from the drag, I had the feeling of stepping out from the calm and into the storm.

The drag was busy as I turned to the left. Down in the main part of the festival it was usually clear on Sunday evening, as the exodus would have begun, and there was that extra little bit of space. Up here, though, on Clapps Lane – the drag that led to the Stones – it was buzzing and looked as busy as ever, so I was hopeful I would sell the remaining bags of green.

However, even after walking through the cafés and across a busy field crowded with people watching a band, I had no luck in getting rid. I made my way back towards the gate that would lead to where a rave was due to happen. Upon reaching the pathway, it was so rammed full of people coming the other way I decided instead to turn left and head down to the main drag.

Walking towards Babylon, I could hear the thump, thump, thump from the beat of music booming from a tent on the other side of the hedge that separated the drag from the field. I continued, intending to turn to the left at the end of the hedge and find the tent from where the noise was coming. Seeing an opening I stopped to take a look.

This proved to be hole in the hedge that countless others had hacked their way through in order to get to the field. As I prepared to go through, I saw that between the hedge and the field there was a five-foot-wide ditch, and at its deepest point it must have been two or three feet. I peered into the gulley. Water was running through it, and, from the look and feel of the earth at the edge, it felt like the bank was muddy. I decided to persist. After being extra careful to avoid slipping and getting covered in mud, I found myself on the other side and right next to an entrance to the tent from which I'd heard the music coming.

It was packed with people raving to a DJ spinning sounds that, along with the strobe lighting, were taking people to places elsewhere, and, judging by the look of many, plenty had already arrived. I began to work my way through those dancing and across in front of the DJ and back around the edge of the main mass of revellers towards the entrance I had just come through.

As I looked at the faces of those on the edge of the dance area, I saw a couple of girls skinning up and decided to try my luck selling them a deal.

'Alright, girls?'

No reply.

'Alright, girls? Any skins?'

One of them offered a packet of Rizla. I took three and handed them back.

'Mind if I stick one here?'

The girl who'd passed the skins took the packet back and nodded her OK. I took out the bag that had become my personal and began to build up. Finishing, I showed the girl the bag and asked if she fancied sticking one herself. She looked at the weed and nodded. It wasn't long before the three of us were chatting away and, not long after that, I'd sold them a bag for £20.

The deal done, I finished my spliff and said ta and my goodbyes. As I turned, a guy approached.

'You serving up?'

I looked at the face behind the voice. He was black, in his twenties and looked like he wanted to be a gangsta, and he was backed up by a couple of his mates. At least I was sure he wasn't

Old Bill. I had three deals left, and I was getting fed up trying to sell them.

I didn't think I should, but I said it anyway, 'I've got three £20 deals of green that I'll do you for £45.'

'Let's see the weed then.'

I showed him my bag of personal and held it up to his nose. He smelled it, sniffed and raised his head slightly.

'Let me see the deals.'

I showed him one that I'd pulled from my pocket.

'You said you had three.'

'Let's see your money,' I replied.

He put his hand into his front pocket and began to pull out a wad of notes. As he did that, I pulled the other two bags from my pocket and put them together with the one that I was already holding. As I held the deals in my palm, from out of nowhere a hand appeared across the front of me and tried to grab the gear, but I was too fast for the snatcher and managed to pull my hand back just in time.

The fact that I'd retracted my hand was the probable reason that, having missed his target, the guy's motion had carried him forward and he stumbled in front of me. I realised that he must have been working with the one who had approached me, and, as his body passed in front of mine, I pushed him towards his accomplices.

I turned and started to run towards the entrance that I'd come through earlier, but not before I saw the guy I'd pushed fall straight into two or three of his companions, and, instead of getting to me, they ended up falling over him. Even so, as I ran, I was aware that there was still one on his feet, and he wasn't that far behind.

I headed straight for the ditch and the hedge I'd negotiated earlier. This time, though, instead of taking my time, I gambled and jumped it in one and, thankfully, landed in one piece on the other side. My pursuer, who had now been joined by his mates, balked at the sight of the jump and was lucky that he wasn't sent into the ditch when one of the others knocked into him after he'd stopped suddenly.

I was away and through the hedge and on to the drag before they had even contemplated crossing the ditch, but, as I turned to look back, one was scrambling up having got across the gap and was on the drag but, even so, I still had a thirty-yard start and headed back up in the direction from which I'd originally come.

As I ran up the slight incline and through the crowds of people, I saw a familiar face coming in my direction. It was a Sheffield guy that I knew from Dorset called Rocky. He was a big lad, standing well over six feet and with matching shoulders. He was with his mate Nigel, another guy from South Yorkshire, who was just an inch or two shorter and of similar build. They saw me running towards them, looked beyond to see four men chasing me and realised that I was in trouble.

From about twenty yards I heard him shout, 'How many of them?'

'Four, I think,' I said, almost out of breath. 'They've just tried to have me off.'

Rocky and Nigel stood ready as, after stopping next to them, I turned to face the four who were chasing me. When my pursuers realised that the numbers were now more even, and they'd seen the size of the two I was with, they stopped dead in their tracks.

'Come on then, big boy,' Rocky said to the one who was nearest.

The four of them looked, thought about it, shuffled awkwardly and just turned and walked away back down the drag they'd just chased me up.

'What happened there then, kid?' Rocky asked me as we turned away ourselves and walked up the drag in the opposite direction.

I explained how I'd come to be chased and then showed him

the weed. He said he liked the look of it. I sold him two of the bags for £25 and put the other 'on the table' and went for a drink with him and Nigel. I couldn't be bothered to go and find Gruff and the others and was happy having a laugh with the men from Yorkshire. At about five on Monday morning I said cheerio to the pair of them and headed back to my tent.

Once there, and as I settled down in my sleeping bag hopeful of a few hours' shut-eye, I was more than happy. Not only had I earned enough to pay H her money back and had a top weekend I would also be going home with around £150. I had enough for a few joints of green, and the lump of hash that I'd stashed would still be there when I woke up to leave. Gruff wouldn't even think I had any weed on me and wouldn't be worried about getting a tug on the way home. I'd done well . . . until, recalling the events at that dance tent, I thought about how lucky I'd been seeing Rocky and Nigel. Had I not run into them, my weekend might have finished somewhat differently.

If only Rocky and Nigel and some of their lot could have been about when I had been captured by Alex. They would have sorted them out alright.

But that was last year, this was the present, and by the time I reached Bristol's main bus station I was breathing deeply and feeling more than a little tense, the memories of last year's escape and that of the previous evening merging together to make my heart miss a beat for what must have been the umpteenth time in the last twenty-four hours. Although I should really have settled for the money I had already made, I was determined, albeit with butterflies in my stomach, that I would carry on grafting and earn some more. All I had to do was make sure that I avoided Alex's crew and keep myself on my toes.

CHAPTER ELEVEN

Making my way into the terminus, I was cheered when I realised that all the people who were there with tents and rucksacks were heading for Glastonbury, which meant the chances were there would be a bus going straight to the festival. That would mean a simple journey back rather than the convoluted route that I had taken in search of a shop selling the pens.

'Is this a queue for a bus to Glastonbury Festival?' I asked a young guy who certainly looked like he was on the way there.

'Yeah, it's £5, pay on the bus.'

'Got a ticket?'

'What, for the bus?'

'No, the festival.'

'Not yet. I reckon I'll get in when I get there.'

'I'll get you in,' I replied. 'Cost you £15.'

'And how's that?'

After giving him a brief rundown, he was still sceptical.

'How do I know it will work?' he said, as he was joined by two of his friends.

Repeating to them what I'd just told him, one of the two who'd turned up a moment earlier spoke.

'I've heard about that,' he said. 'Matthew called me on Wednesday evening and said that was how he'd got in. Sarah, Shaun and Louise were with him, and they had no problems either.'

'I'm still not sure . . .' said the first guy.

'Tell you what I'll do,' I said, trying to take the initiative. 'I'll stamp you up now for a fiver. I'll be working the gate nearest to where the bus drops us off, and you can come with me, and if it doesn't work I'll give you your money back. But, if you don't take a chance now and get there, see it working on someone else and come back to me then, it will cost you at least a tenner, but probably fifteen.'

'I'll take a chance on that. A fiver you say?' said the third guy, and with that the first two followed his lead. I stamped them up, ensuring I left them confident enough to trust me that I'd be at the gate as I told them I would, and took their £5 notes.

There were seventy or eighty people at the bus station who were waiting for the special Glastonbury buses, and there were plenty among that number who, like the three I'd just stamped, were travelling without a festival ticket. Instilling even more confidence about my honesty in the three guys, I asked them if they would mind looking after my rucksack and place in the queue while I went to see if there was anyone else who wanted to use of my services.

Most of the people I asked were, at first, sceptical, but my by now well-rehearsed patter persuaded most of those who showed some interest, and, once I had walked the queue, I'd earned another £100 stamping up twenty people on the 'special £5 advance-rate deal'.

The buses laid on for the festival had still not returned from transporting their earlier customers, and there would, we were told by a company official, be a delay of at least half an hour until the next ones would be ready to take those of us who were waiting. Asking the first three guys I'd stamped if they wanted anything to drink, I found a café and bought some food, a drink for myself and the can of Coke and two bottles of water the three lads wanted.

Taking what I'd ordered, I looked for a seat and saw an unoccupied table next to one that had four young guys sitting around it. I shuffled over to the empty table and sat down, began to eat, relaxing but with my mind and senses still alert from the buzz of making money. In my head I was again counting what I'd made, while physically sorting out what cash I had on me. There was

£2,150 at the camp with H and in my tent, £50 in my money-belt, £100 from just now and about £20 left from the money that Alex had allowed me to keep. Without even thinking about it, I put the £100 with the £50 safely away in my money-belt, and the rest of the notes and loose coins in my jeans pocket.

I was about to look into the future – well, the end of the day, at least – and optimistically started to calculate how many people, and at what price, I would have to get in to reach the £3,000 mark, but my train of thought was interrupted when one of the four on the table next to me began to voice his doubts about making the trek to Glastonbury.

'I don't want to go all the way down there and not get in,' he argued, the other three listening sympathetically. 'I do want to go, but I want to be 100 per cent sure that I'll get in, and I'd rather try to buy a ticket.'

'There aren't any left,' said two of the others in unison.

'We're still going,' said a third. 'We'll be OK.'

'Look,' said the doubtful one, 'I don't want to put you guys on a downer. It's been a shit day so far, and I just don't want it getting any worse.'

'I can get you in,' I said, once his last statement had been digested by the other three.

They glanced over, and I told them about the stamp and my special deal. One, a round-faced lad aged of about twenty, with a mop of ginger hair, responded in the affirmative. He was well-spoken, as were his companions, giving me the impression they were probably students.

'Sounds great. I'll try that,' he said in a cheerful manner and extended his arm.

'Keep it low,' I whispered as the gaze of the café proprietor came our way, Ginger immediately withdrawing his limb and folding his arms.

Once the café owner had ensured that things were running

smoothly and was satisfied all his customers were happy and that the waitresses had done their jobs and had kept up with the task of clearing the used cutlery and crockery from the tables, his attention was then taken up with checking the till receipts.

I nodded to Ginger, and he again placed his forearm on the table. I stamped him up, and then we exchanged seats so I could do the same to his friends. Two of the three remaining put their arms on the table, but the guy who had his doubts about going without a ticket refused my offer and remained motionless save a shake of his head.

'Come on, Tom, what's up?' asked Ginger, but Tom just stared ahead.

'Can't go wrong risking a fiver,' said one of the other two.

'How do I know, how do *you* know that he isn't going to rip us off?' said Tom, talking to his friends but looking at me.

'That's a bit rude,' I retorted, the suppressed anger from earlier reigniting as a dark part of my mind looked for a victim, someone I could exact some kind of retribution for the events of the previous evening.

Ginger, fearing that I might, having taken offence, now block his and his friends' entry to the festival, turned to me and pleaded, 'Don't worry about him, he's just a bit upset.' Nodding his head as if pointing to the pair that had taken a stamp, he continued, 'We trust you. We've got no problems with it.'

'Cheers, mate, thank you,' I replied while telling myself to calm down. 'I'll see you there. You getting in the queue for the bus?'

'We'll be out in a minute,' he answered as I stood to leave.

Giving the other two a look of acknowledgement, I walked out and back to the queue and the guys who were holding my place. Giving them their drinks, one explained that he'd been to the telephone box and called one of his friends who said he, along with a few others, would also fancy a weekend at Glastonbury for a fiver. After repeating the terms of the deal, I invented a new offer that would, if they turned up, see them pay a special advanced rate of £7.50 per head as long as there were four or more.

After hearing me out, he accepted the offer, albeit by proxy on his friends' behalf, borrowed some change from one of the others and ran back to the phone box to call his mate. He was back within a couple of minutes and said that there would be at least seven coming, they'd be at the bus station within the hour and, if they missed the bus that we were on, they'd probably be on the next one and would meet me outside the gate at Glastonbury.

'Would you wait for them?' he asked, somewhat timidly.

I nodded.

'Yeah, I'll wait for them,' I said, immediately switching on to the fact that an hour or two's wait outside the festival by the nearest entrance to where the organised special buses were running wouldn't be a bad idea, especially if I had the same ratio of customers as I'd had at the bus station.

I had earned £115 in less than forty minutes from twenty-three customers and had the prospect of another £57.50 to come if the seven advance bookings showed. From what the woman in the ultraviolet pen shop had said, I assumed there would be loads of people now on the stamp, and I would have to swallow taking a serious reduction in revenue if I was going to undercut the others and get any business.

From earning an average of about £20 per person until now, including those that I'd got in for Alex, I was now weighing up whether to go for broke and just ask £10 per head. I'd have to work hard if I wanted the three grand I had set my sights on, but, at the end of the day, a dollar was a dollar, and £10 it would be.

The sound of a double-decker bus pulling into the station made everyone in the now snaking queue look up from what they were doing to see if it was the one for which they had been waiting. It was, and as we moved down the line, getting closer to the embarkation point, the anxious expressions of those towards the middle and further back changed to looks of relief as another two buses pulled into the yard, parking behind the one that was already taking passengers on board.

The arrival of these two buses did nothing to help the until-then orderly line of people waiting for their ride. The queue split with those nearest the doors of the newly parked-up buses suddenly finding themselves at the front of another two lines of people who were starting to jostle their way forward. Matters were further complicated when a bus company employee tried to make everybody queue up in their original places. One of the guys who'd been looking after my bag had made it to the door and was nearly on board, but it looked as if there might not be enough room for me or his two friends. Looking at the bus at the back, I could see there were fewer people queuing for it, so I decided to try my luck and get on that one.

I turned to one of the three, the one I'd first spoken to. 'I'm getting on that one,' I said, pointing to the last bus. 'Cheers, lads, see you there.'

The two of them nodded, and I fought my way through the crush of people waiting to get on. Within minutes I was sitting upstairs on the top deck with a window seat to myself.

There was a little cheer and a hooray from some as the driver pushed the button to close the door, the hiss of hydraulics telling us that we were on our way. In convoy style, the three buses departed, leaving the bus station virtually deserted, the squalid grey concrete no longer given life and colour by those who had been occupying its passenger walkways, with all those waiting for a ride to Glastonbury on their way.

Soon the outskirts of Bristol were replaced by the Somerset countryside, and, with the roads relatively clear, we made good time. It was now a boiling-hot day, and people naturally opened the windows to let in some fresh air. Sitting halfway down, I became aware of the smell of hash as people started skinning up.

'Time for work,' I thought.

There was a couple in the seats in front of me. I sat on the edge of mine and, half in the aisle, leaned forward.

'You OK for tickets?'

'Thanks, man, we're OK,' said the guy sitting on the inside, the girl next to the window repeating the sentiment.

'Nice one.'

I was about to stand when the girl sitting on the left-hand side of the divide caught my attention by way of a tap on my arm.

'Are you selling tickets?'

'No, but I can get you in.'

She was with three others, and they all took a chance, appreciating the benefit of the £5 deal but getting away with giving me £18 in change to save themselves breaking into their notes. I was back in business with money again at the forefront of my mind. Walking down to the front, I first asked the people on the right of the aisle, then turned and went towards the back, asking those on the other side.

By the time I passed the point at which I'd started, I'd earned another £35, a total of £165 from the bus customers, and I was starting to feel a lot better about the way things had turned out. Even though I was only making a fiver a head, it was better than nothing. The feel of £5, £10 and £20 notes in my hand was again making me feel as if earning money was an addiction, my mind with this insatiable craving for getting more, more and more.

After trying my luck at the rear of the upper deck and then downstairs, I had earned another £35, making it a nice round £200 from the £5 deals. I still had the £50 plus the rest of the money I'd started the day with, and £15 in £1 coins and smash I didn't bother to count. Returning to my seat, I ensured that the £250 in notes I had in my money-belt was secure, made myself comfortable and smoked a joint.

Being on the top deck of the bus enabled me to see the

picturesque countryside through which we were passing, with those downstairs limited to just a ground-level view of the hedgerows and garden walls of the houses outside. As I gazed at the fields and meadows, their greens and yellows exaggerated by the brilliance of the sun, scenery that in other circumstances would have engendered a relaxed calm was suddenly darkened as my mind suddenly switched back to Alex, his crew and the previous night.

I was now thinking how good I would feel if I could get my own back on the robbing, spiteful, bullying cunts. I'd love it if they got smashed everywhere, a proper spanking, with every punch and kick reminding them that they should have stuck to what they know on their own manor and leave ordinary people like me, who were doing people a genuine nice turn, alone.

I thought of 1987 when, after turning up at a festival in considerable numbers, a massive crew of blacks went up to the travellers' field to tax a bunch of people who they thought would be a pushover. Much of the illicit hash, weed, speed and acid that was on sale originated from the confines of the travellers' field, something that had obviously upset the posse who'd gone up to smash them, their profit margins having seriously suffered because the travellers were in possession of the best gear on the site.

Most of the travellers were extremely paranoid when it came to meeting strangers, and the sight of some forty or fifty black guys entering their space did nothing else but to alert them to the threat that they posed. The mob moved through the gate and to the right side of the drag along which some of the travellers had set up their vans and trucks and began to turn over the chairs and tables that had been set up in front of several vehicles that were serving teas and coffees and various forms of hallucinatory drugs.

Within seconds the commotion had caused the entire occupancy of the drag, and many from the vans and tents behind both sides of it, to turn out and confront the invaders. The bunch of crusties, hippies or whatever else the blacks used to describe them as, were in no mood to be walked over, and they battered their enemy everywhere, with the women joining in and letting their anger out as they waded in wielding spades and shovels, cooking pans and trying to hurt as many as they could. Within no more than a couple of minutes the blacks were being run back through the gate at the bottom of the field and on through the other side like bees flying from their nest, and then running in all directions in twos and threes and as far away as they had to go before the defenders were satisfied that the invasion had been repulsed and gave up the chase.

Of those who couldn't run and were lying on the ground, groaning and weeping from the pain their injuries were causing them, not one was shown any mercy by the defenders, as each and every one of them was treated to another brutal kicking, their heads getting saucepans and ladles wrapped around them before they were dragged out of the field and dumped in the adjoining meadow and then just left there, covered in blood as well as a good coating of piss and spit that came courtesy of the victors.

All in all, it was a fair result, with common-sense justice prevailing and the bad guys getting a hiding, but the travellers weren't exactly angels themselves. Those who had just joined battle were the remnants of the underground movement that sprang up in the early 1980s, when any group of people in brightly painted vans, old coaches and other such vehicles living on the road were labelled part of the Peace Convoy.

The original Peace Convoy evolved through a mix of women involved in the Greenham Common Airbase protests between 1981 and 1983 and peaceable travellers who lived their lives on the road or from festival to festival. While gypsies are often referred to as 'travellers', the term also applied to those who followed the culture of the movement that was spawned as a result of the Greenham protesters.

Although a few relied on DHSS giros for their income, many

were self-sufficient and adept at living on one of the many converted buses, coaches, lorries, ambulances and the like that were prevalent among people who had been tagged New Age Travellers.

At the time, and especially in the countryside of counties such as Berkshire, Wiltshire, Somerset, Devon and Dorset, it wasn't uncommon to see one or two, or sometimes six or seven, such vehicles parked up in a lay-by, the stretch of that part of the road being used as a temporary stop-off point before they continued their journey to whichever festival or gathering they were heading towards. Over the course of the summer months, the groups of six or seven vehicles sometimes saw their numbers swollen by others who had joined them either at a festival or along the way.

Many of the people involved just wanted to enjoy a simple life, their idealistic dream to live with as little impact as possible on the environment. Although they would have undoubtedly been scorned by a vast swathe of the general public for their lifestyle, there were many families on the road, their children being brought up to learn how to build a fire and keep warm in the winter, as well as being taught about life in the countryside rather than going out playing in the streets of towns and cities or sitting indoors watching TV.

The hippy label that was attached to the convoy came with the fact that many were vegetarian and plenty were vegan, and, of course, they weren't bothered about conventional fashion. They created their own, wearing brightly coloured hats and knitted jumpers they made themselves and hand-me-downs and second-hand clothes which fitted in perfectly with the feather-cut dreadlocks or spiked hair and nose, eye, lip and face piercings that many displayed.

The idealistic image of the New Age Traveller began to lose its credibility as those on the road were joined, circa early 1984, by a younger breed, many of who had given up squatting houses and flats in the inner cities and exchanged their brick and concrete homes for tents, tepees and vans, following in the footsteps of their older and, on the whole, more laid-back and wiser contemporaries. The traveller fraternity soon became permeated by the younger rogue element that thought nothing of breaking into a field, setting up a camp and then liberating whatever they could find from any house or building that was in the area.

Then, life on the dole was an option that was easy to get used to, and in the days when unemployment benefit was paid out by means of a giro cheque, those who had registered as 'no fixed abode' could claim their weekly entitlement at any DHSS office in the country. Those who had joined the convoy would, once a week, either on a Thursday or a Friday, head for the nearest benefit office to where they were camped to pick up their cheques.

Once their giros were collected and cashed, these individuals attached to the various convoys would hit the nearest supermarket or off-licence, buying up cider and extra-strong lager and often continue a thieving spree that had begun in those post offices that also served as local shops, thereby extending their anti-social habits from where they camped to the nearest village or town.

As a consequence this brought them to the attention of the various local constabularies, but catching them in the act was an extremely rare occurrence, and usually the locals who had suffered were, despite the damage and loss of property, relieved just to see the back of them. Meantime, the local police forces were content to keep moving them on, happy to be passing the buck to some of their colleagues in another county. However, it would only be a matter of time before those on the move found somewhere else along the road to set up, and, in some cases, the police were having to deal with the same people several times in the same day. Scores of travellers and a great number from the now many convoys would be regulars at the annual summer solstice at Stonehenge, the beginning of June seeing a slow trickle begin to travel along the

A303 to the site of the ancient monument. By the second and third week of the month, the sight of convoys of four and five vehicles making their way into Wiltshire to join those already at Stonehenge preparing to celebrate the longest day of the year was common.

It is said druids have been performing a sun-worshipping ritual there since the days when the ancient monument was erected, and in the late 1960s and throughout the 1970s the solstice at Stonehenge became a special site for the original hippies, a place of calm and mystery. By 1983, however, the druids paying homage to the rising sun were merely a backdrop to the free festival that had evolved over the years. With the explosion in the drug scene, and more and more of the younger population of the country beginning to discover acid, speed and cocaine along with cannabis, the Stonehenge Festival was not only an entirely unpoliced event but also a haven for those using illicit substances.

The absence of the police ensured that drugs, alcohol and revelry were the order of the day, with some of those who were there for the duration – usually between three to five weeks – setting up cafés and bars to cater for the demand for food and drink. Along the drags people sat in front of their tents and sold hash, the deals being weighed up in front of customers on the sets of scales that advertised the fact they were selling cannabis. They would do any deal required, including selling ounces, fours, nine-bars, some even having enough wrapped around them to punt a weight, or a kilo.

The early 1980s had seen the re-emergence of acid, a drug that came to prominence in the 1960s. Although acid could seriously affect the state of a person's mind, once it had worn off normality returned, and it was considered a clean, uncut drug when put alongside speed and cocaine, becoming a popular choice for many who enjoyed the festival-and-travelling life.

Acid in the form of what were known as microdots had just come on to the scene, the latest improvement to the then very common form of consuming the drug by way of a blotter, which were individual tabs of acid that had designs on them such as a sunrise or a star or a Batman bat or whatever the chemist or supplier had chosen for his product.

The process of producing the tabs was relatively easy. A sheet of suitable paper having been printed with squares on it, each featuring the relevant design and no more than a quarter of an inch in size, then had liquid acid dripped on to it by way of an eye-drop or, if they were the best, dunked for a second or two in the receptacle containing the chemical with the paper getting a good soaking. Once the sheet had dried, the tablets were ready for distribution and sale.

A microdot, on the other hand, was basically a stronger type of acid but marketed in a different form. Each microdot was like a tiny breadcrumb, coloured black or a very dark brown. Extremely fragile, before consumption they had to be handled with care to avoid being dropped as, once on the floor, especially outdoors, they were extremely hard, if not impossible, to find.

One year at Stonehenge a friend of mine called Reedy, who'd joined the main Peace Convoy, had a roaring trade going in what he described as a 'psycho-toot'. This was a concoction that consisted of a line of either speed or cocaine – whatever your fancy – and a microdot that was crushed up and cut in with the powder, the price set by which of the powders the buyer preferred. He had all the kit he required to sell on the move and was known as Deals On Wheels due to the fact that he was making his way around the festival on a motorbike, a scrambler he'd bought for £50 on site.

You could do what you wanted at Stonehenge as long as you didn't tread on anyone's toes. The same year, a few of the top faces from a large Dorset town went along and set up a beer tent from which they were selling pints of draught beer and lager. One was a club owner whose venue was not too far from the town's square and was a haunt for the hundreds of Scousers and other assorted northerners who had decided to live in the south-coast resort. He was very well connected and wasn't to be crossed, and he held the respect of everyone who frequented his club, which was partly due to him allowing the open use of drugs.

You could go there some nights and smell the hash as you queued to get in, and, with a lot of the local dealers using the club as a venue from which to sell their drugs, it became one of the main places to go if you wanted to score after the pubs had kicked out. It also became a refuge for those partaking in a host of other criminal activities, including shoplifting, petty theft, burglary and robbery and, more often than not, it stayed open far longer than the 1am closure the council insisted applied to all nightclubs. The said club owner certainly knew how to tread on the wrong side of the law, and he knew his way about.

This particular year, when Stonehenge started, he'd hired a van and packed the back of it with a marquee, tables, chairs, a couple of sofas, beer and lager barrels and pumps, all taken from his club, and created a mini version of his place in Dorset at the festival. He was a big bloke, Sheffield born, and was there with Rocky – the guy who stood by me when I was being chased at Glastonbury – and a few of his closest mates. It was all going well until he, along with everybody else, apparently rejected a tax demand from a group of Hell's Angels.

I wasn't there when it happened, as I'd returned to Dorset on a mission and stayed over, preferring to travel back to Stonehenge the next day. When I did return to the festival, the story of what had occurred was the first thing I heard, even before the person who I'd run the errand to Dorset for had asked whether it was 'job done' and had I managed to transport the nine-bar of Moroccan hash safely.

Sure enough, later that evening when I walked up the drag where the club owner's makeshift bar had once been, all that remained was a burnt patch of grass, piles of ashes, lumps of half-cindered wood and melted plastic that had once been a table or a chair. He had escaped, though, as had his mates, fighting their way out against superior numbers of mainly bikers, unscathed but leaving Stonehenge for a forty-minute drive back to Dorset and safety. The rest of us, only involved in his festival venture by way of knowing him and drinking there, stayed on in peace, enjoying the party for the next two weeks.

That was the way the law was at a place like Stonehenge and many of the other festivals of the time, but the life of a traveller and the gigs themselves became an increasingly attractive option for many, and the phenomenon flourished. In between festivals, and when there was nothing else on, the smaller groups of travellers began to link up with others, and, once they had found a suitable farm or piece of common land, they would set up camp and start their own mini festivals, the original forerunners of the many thousands of free and illegal raves and warehouse parties that hundreds of thousands of British youngsters subsequently attended and still attend to this day.

Within eighteen months or so, and after a winter that had seen travellers making permanent camps in parts of Wales, the Peace Convoy began to grow into two distinct groups. The genuine and original set stayed more or less loyal to each other, sticking together on the road and in camps while they tried to distance themselves from a faction that saw various hard-line anarchists and animal-rights protesters joining the ranks of an extreme division of the travelling fraternity looking for cover so they could hide from the gaze of Special Branch and other internal security services, while seeking out new recruits for their causes. Known as the Brew Crew, this motley collection of society's outcasts was also often referred to as the Mutants.

Forming a convoy of their own, the Brew Crew had acquired their name due to their liking for intravenous drug misuse – jacking up speed – and keeping their thirst quenched with cans of Carlsberg

Special Brew lager and strong cider. After constant self-abuse by way of their use of dirty drugs and excess alcohol, and funded by the welfare state, the Brew Crew instilled a definite sense of unease and insecurity wherever they went.

One look at them told you everything you needed to know. Their personas displayed intravenous drug misuse, with the pale, bad condition of their skin underlining their habits, the pin-and-ink self-drawn tattoos a dark shade of dirty blue, almost black, against their skinny arms and necks and sometimes faces. When speaking to anyone outside of their group, conversation was usually limited to the language of drug dealing or trying to beg or put themselves into a position where they could take advantage of the people they were talking to.

Their underhand ways and habits oozed out of every pore of their skin, along with the smell of alcohol-infused sweat that clung to the combat trousers and camouflage jackets they commonly wore, but most of all they had the stench of trouble permanently accompanying them.

Shunned and avoided by decent festival-goers like the plague, and totally rejected by the decent travellers – perhaps their last link to the rest of society – the Brew Crew lowered themselves to a state where they gained a reputation for thieving at festivals and even lying in wait as other groups of travellers would go into town to collect their giros before moving into their unguarded campsites and stealing valuables such as money, jewellery, drugs and anything else they fancied, including children's clothes and toys. They were, in short, a bunch of scumbags. They were a small minority compared with the total number of people who lived on the road, yet still a sizeable enough group of undesirables not only to smear the reputation of the majority but also to stir Middle England and the Tory Party into action.

After winning the 1983 election, due in part to the Falklands factor, the second consecutive term of the Conservative Party saw

Margaret Thatcher continue her government's moves to limit the power of the trade unions, while positioning herself for a fight with Arthur Scargill, leader of the National Union Of Mineworkers.

The miners' strike that began in 1984 and subsequent police action was a jolt to a nation that, only two years earlier, had seemed united when Thatcher gave orders for the Royal Navy to set sail with an armed force to recapture South Georgia and the Falkland Islands from Argentine invaders who were foolish enough to try to take the sovereign British territories in the South Atlantic Ocean.

The dispute involving the mineworkers was a protest that saw the strikers involved in toe-to-toe, running and sometimes very violent clashes with the massed ranks of the police, their number made up of officers drawn from various constabularies across the UK mainland, there to help the scabs and blacklegs who were breaking the strike and crossing picket lines.

By the time March 1985 came, and flushed with success after she had used the police as a tool of the state to brutally smash the miners into submission during the course of their year-long strike, Prime Minster Margaret Thatcher then turned her attention to those who were next in her sights, an 'underclass' that was purposely unemployed, the people who were, in the eyes of the government, abusing the benefit system.

While Thatcher, along with Ronald Reagan, took the Cold War fight to the Soviets externally, on the home front the first in line for a volley from the state, backed by an increased majority within the House Of Commons, were the travellers, the next biggest threat from within after the Greenham Common, anti-Cruise-Missile protesters.

On 1 June 1985, three months after the official end of the mineworkers' strike, Wiltshire Police led an operation that would ultimately see the demise of the convoy. After the authorities had imposed a four-mile exclusion zone around Stonehenge, a large body of travellers set out from their camp in Savernake Forest on the Marlborough-to-Salisbury road to try to reach the stones.

Once the convoy vehicles had left the forest, police moved in behind them and dumped several tons of gravel on the road in order to block any chance they might have to return. They then blocked the road ahead of the convoy, and officers began to attack the vehicles and their occupants who were at the front of the line.

With those who could escape running back down the road and warning others what was happening, some of the travellers towards the front of the now stationary convoy drove into a field and were soon followed by many of their companions. Once inside the confines of the field, there was a short stand-off between the police and the travellers before the men in uniform attacked and went on to smash their way to disabling almost every vehicle in the field, leaving the majority of the 440 detained travellers homeless, their worldly possessions strewn everywhere.

The police action against the convoy that day became known as the Battle Of The Beanfield and has subsequently been viewed as one of the worst examples of wanton police violence and abuse of power since the foundation of the modern British service.

In the days that followed, Maggie Thatcher, talking of her cabinet, said they were 'only too delighted to do anything we can to make life difficult for such things as hippy convoys', and her then Home Secretary Douglas Hurd labelled the travellers as 'nothing more than a band of medieval brigands who have no respect for the law or the rights of others'.

Nine days after the massacre at the Beanfield, the Hampshire Constabulary moved in to break up a site that had been set up by travellers who, denied access to Stonehenge, had managed to avoid the police forces of several counties to gather at Stoney Cross, a few miles west of Southampton.

There, the police made a further sixty-four arrests and impounded 129 vehicles, but fortunately for the travellers word had reached them of the raid and many made good their escape, rendering the care orders for the children that the authorities intended to use useless, as all their offspring were with those who'd managed to avoid the constabulary's action.

The following year the government successfully introduced the Public Order Act, 1986, legislation that made it illegal for more than twelve vehicles to park up together and giving the police the power to break up any such gathering.

While the Thatcher regime rode the crest of the wave of plaudits directed towards it for its actions in eradicating the scourge that were the travellers by a grateful public that had been too readily and easily influenced by a government-friendly press, the end result was a rekindling of the acquaintance between the Brew Crew and the rest of the convoy, their uneasy alliance now seeing them co-exist not too far away from each other, either on the road or at a festival.

By the time 1987 came, and the crew of gangstas had gone to tax the hardcore travellers, little did they know they would be taking on a battle-hardened community that had years of experience in looking after themselves.

As it drove over a bump in the road, the bus on which I was travelling from Bristol momentarily lurched to one side, bringing my thoughts back to the immediate present. As I had done when my mind slipped back to that time when Rocky rescued me at last year's festival, I wished that Alex and his cronies would run into a mob of the same calibre of travellers as the lot that battered the taxmen all those years ago.

If only, I repeated in my mind.

Looking again at the view of the passing countryside, my eyes began to get heavy, and it must have been then that I drifted off to sleep.

CHAPTER TWELVE

'We're here. Wake up, we're here.'

My eyes opened as I felt the hand of the girl across the aisle shake my shoulder.

'Cheers,' I replied, fighting the urge to drift back into sleep, but, once I'd stretched my legs, arms and shoulders, I felt fine. The girl smiled at me.

'Thanks for that,' she said, referring to the stamp that I'd given her.

I smiled back. She was aged about twenty-three, maybe twenty-four, slim with tied-back curly brown hair and lovely blue eyes. She was a real looker, but it wasn't as if I was going to pull her. All the same, she was gorgeous and a nice sight to open my eyes to.

'Have a really nice time,' I said. I had to get to work.

I was pleased the buses dropped everyone off quite close to the festival site, and I headed straight for Gate 2. I had told everybody that I'd stamped in Bristol and on the way that I would be there, and with the promise of the advance bookings it wouldn't be long before I'd be adding another £50 to my earnings.

There were loads of people making their way along the same path as me. Some had obviously been there a day or two, just walking from where they'd camped to inside the festival, and it was easy to see they weren't new arrivals. Unlike most of the people walking down the lane, they weren't weighed down with tents, rucksacks and the like.

Of those who were just arriving, there was a large percentage burdened by extremely heavy bags and rucksacks, and, even before they got to where they were going to camp, they realised they had brought too much luggage. With long, miserable faces flushed from the heat, and with sweat running down from their foreheads and into their eyes, their various items of baggage were proving weighty and awkward to carry – and the worst bit was, once the weekend was over, they'd have to carry most of it back.

Some turned up with wheelbarrows, some sturdier than others, and these weren't a bad option, especially if a person arrived at one side of the festival site but wanted to stay on the other. A lot of kit went into a decent builder's barrow, but, of course, it had to be brought to Glastonbury in the first place, something that was impossible on public transport.

Every now and again, along the length of the path, there would be a broken axle from either a luggage trolley or another type of carrier that, within minutes of being too heavily loaded with cargo, buckled from the strain. Or wheels fitted for use on pavements and in stations and airports that proved to be too small to cope with the country lanes and hard, stony ground at Glastonbury.

At the other extreme, there were young lads who, attending the festival for the first time and fuelled by stories they'd heard from friends who had been in previous years, turned up with just the clothes they were dressed in, but with three, four or, if they could manage it, five crates of twenty-four cans of lager, beer or cider. What state they would be in by the time it turned freezing cold in the middle of the night or, even worse, a day later when they had been sweating in the sun for sixteen hours – and with nothing to wash with or fresh clothes to change into – was anybody's guess.

There were plenty of people milling about as I reached the point where the lane from where we'd been dropped off crossed the path that ran around the perimeter fence, and I found myself not too far away from the top of the path that would lead down to Gate 2. From there it wasn't a long walk to where those entering the festival site would have to show the stewards their tickets and pass-out stamps. It would be an ideal place to pick up business, with people heading in from the direction I had just come from as well as from the left and the right. If I worked around the cross-roads, I'd have a fairly good view from a distance of who was coming from each of the three directions, an important consideration when it came to avoiding Alex and his crew.

After momentarily pausing to reflect upon my choice of location, I continued down the path towards Gate 2. I wanted to check out the stewards and the gate itself to satisfy myself it was safe to proceed. Along the length of both sides of the fence that bordered the entry gate, people milled about, some waiting to meet friends, others just stopping to have a smoke or a drink. Others sat there with their still unpacked bags and tents looking wistfully at those walking past.

'Hey!'

I turned in the direction of the voice to see it was Ginger, one of the guys from the café in Bristol.

'Hey, how'ya doing? Been through yet?'

'Not yet,' he replied. 'We're still trying to sort something out for our friend.'

I looked over his shoulder to where he'd pointed and saw his three friends sitting on the grass at the side of the path. The one without a ticket was still looking fairly upset and nervous.

'I'll give you a hand in if you want.'

'Cheers,' he said, and we walked over to his companions.

Nodding in acknowledgement, I joined them squatting down on my haunches to talk. Ignoring the fact that one was still undecided, I explained the plan of action.

'Two of you wait here with your bags. I'll leave mine and take two in with me. We'll come straight back once we've got through and then swap, and once you've been in and got the proper stamp on the way out, you'll have no worries.'

Ginger stayed with the bags while the other two I'd stamped came with me. We went through the gate without a hitch, and, after the regulation wait until we went back out, we returned to Ginge and the other one within five minutes.

The two I'd just taken through didn't need to tell their friends that it had worked. The smiles on their faces showed their delight, and a look of hope flashed across the face of the guy who'd refused a £5 deal in the café and to who I had said the charge would be at least a tenner if I stamped him at the festival.

'Please . . .' said Ginger, looking first at me and then at his mate, his request delivered with just the hint of a plea while the other two went quiet.

'Go on then,' I replied, 'a fiver. Show me your arm.'

He put his arm forward, and £5 was in his hand. I took the money, applied the mark and repeated the magic words, and with Ginger he walked down to the gate with me while the other two remained where they were, looking after the bags.

Staying inside for the length of time it took me to build a joint, we turned and walked back through the exit aisle, and the kid I'd just stamped offered his thanks and went ahead up the incline towards the others who were waiting with their kit. Heading to where I'd decided I would work from, I walked up the slope with Ginger.

'You've made my day,' he said. 'Thank you so much.'

'I've made your day? How's that?'

'You've made my day because . . . this morning . . . this morning I had a ticket for Glastonbury, but I lost it.'

'What?' I exclaimed. 'This morning you had a ticket, and you lost it?'

'That's right,' he sighed, shaking his head slightly, the disbelief that he had mislaid it returning and clearly showing on his face.

Putting my hand inside my back pocket where I had just put the fiver I'd taken from his friend, I pulled it out and handed it to him along with two £10 notes.

'Here, take this.'

He looked surprised and embarrassed, his head dropping slightly.

'I couldn't . . .'

'Take it, mate. Have a nice time,' I replied, pressing the notes into his palm.

Although he took it reluctantly, he was genuinely grateful and went on to explain that, being a student at university, the £58 that he'd paid for the ticket had cut a large hole in his finances, and he only had another £50 to last him the weekend at the festival. No wonder he'd been so keen to accept a £5 deal.

We reached his friends, who were already standing and loaded up, their rucksacks on their backs, and the one holding my bag offered it to me.

'Good luck, guys,' I said, addressing them all as we shook hands and went our separate ways, the four of them chatting excitedly and obviously relishing the prospect of the weekend to come.

Giving the kid his money back and a few quid on top didn't bother me. After all, it was only £25, and I'd made over two grand. I had been making loads of money – easy money – and it was good karma to spread a little bit about.

Over the years I had been to loads of festivals, gigs, Chelsea matches and things like that without a ticket, and, if I didn't have to blag my way in, it was because someone had given me a freebie, someone in the same frame of mind as myself, showing the same generosity to me as I'd shown Ginge. Yes, it was good to give a little bit back.

They walked off down towards the gate, and, going up the slope, I passed a group of four who were sitting at the side of the path.

'You lot been in yet?'

Each of them, in unison, sorrowfully shook their heads and returned my enquiry by way of a vacant, mournful stare.

'Do you mind if I sit down a minute?'

It didn't take me long to persuade them to take a chance on the stamp, and, at £35 for the four, they were getting a bargain. It was the same for them as it had been with Ginge and his mates, two coming in and the other two waiting and then taking their turn with me helping them through with their bags on the second trip before collecting the money. For an hour or so I didn't have to move from the approach to the gate to get my trade, and, having just success-fully guided another two people in at £10 each, thereby bringing the total I'd earned from that stretch alone to £130, I again made my way out of the festival and on up the slope. As the back of my legs began to take the strain of walking up the incline, I noticed a guy who looked as if he was heading straight for me.

'Remember me?' he asked, as he came closer. 'Bristol Bus Station . . . you said you'd be able to get our friends in.'

I recognised him and stopped.

'Hello, mate. Are they here?'

It was one of the guys who'd looked after my bag at the bus depot, and, sure enough, as he told me they would, his friends had arrived and were waiting at the top of the lane near the crossroads. Like Ginge and his mates, this lot were also students, living in Bristol and attending the city's university. It was to one of them that the call at the bus station had been made. Word spread around the hall of residence where he lived, and news of the £7.50 entrance fee had tempted all who were there. Within half an hour of hearing about the stamp, there were eleven of them at the bus station waiting for a ride to the Glastonbury Festival.

Agreeing a concessionary fee of £70 for everyone, and leaving them to work out to the penny exactly how much it would cost individually, I took the first four through, and, as usual, brought them back. This time, though, as I walked through exit barriers I noticed one of the gate supervisors giving me a look, as if he thought I was up to no good. When we returned to the spot where the others were waiting, I changed my shirt, which was light green, to a short-sleeved blue polo shirt and replaced the dark-blue base-ball hat I was wearing with one that was cream coloured. I also donned a pair of sunglasses.

I returned through the gate with the next four and passed right in front of the steward who'd been eyeing me suspiciously, but he didn't seem to notice me, and while those who'd just come through returned to their friends immediately, I chose to wait, explaining that I would roll a J and have a quick smoke and would be along for the last three of their party shortly.

I wasn't worried that the first eight had been in and hadn't yet paid me. There were those other three outside, and they would be going nowhere until I got back – and, anyway, as they were still debating how much they would each have to chip in to fund their entry, I thought I'd give them a little more time to work it out. At £70 for eleven they were making a saving, but being skint students, every penny was important. I had shaved off £1.14 per person against the £7.50 they were expecting to pay, but with that equalling £69.96 they were probably going through their change to find exactly the right amount, as well as arguing about who would be generous enough to put the extra 4p in to make it up to £70.

I finished my smoke and flicked the roach, the effect of the hash hitting me as I stood, and, albeit a little unsteadily, walked to within sight of the gate and went over to the side where there was a short queue of people waiting to be stamped out as they left.

As I waited my turn, there was a bit of a commotion starting on the entry side where the gate supervisor who'd been clocking me a few minutes earlier and another three stewards were getting involved with a guy trying to get in.

'I've already been in and come out,' he protested.

'How many times?' demanded the supervisor.

Unsure of exactly what to say, he mumbled, 'Loads, at least four or five.'

'Today?'

'Yes, today. Why?'

'Had a wash?'

The question baffled him.

'Had a wash?' he repeated. 'Why should I have had a wash?'

'Because,' replied the supervisor confidently, 'it might explain why I can only see part of a mark when I put your arm under the light, and what you've got there looks like it's been done by someone outside.'

Grabbing him by his collar, the supervisor pulled the man forward past where I was standing and handed him to two of the waiting stewards, who promptly marched him through the two lines of barriers and into the festival, then immediately back out again down an exit that that the security teams reserved for Glastonbury staff or those caught trying to bunk in. They were on to the fake stamps.

Although I knew the gate supervisors and their staff would now be extra vigilant when checking people's marks, I put the fact that the guy had been caught down to bad craftsmanship by the person who'd drawn the stamp, as well as not leaving his bags behind. Maybe he was on his own, but it didn't matter. Whatever the reason for him being knocked back, all I knew was that my job had become a little bit harder.

After returning to collect the last of the advanced bookings and returning through the gate again, it was noticeable that the stewards inspecting the stamps were doing so with a far keener interest than they had been doing previously. Nevertheless, and true to form, the three I was taking in got through without a hitch, and, after walking a suitable distance away from the gate, I collected my £70 fee and left them to go out and back to the rest of their friends themselves while I stayed on the inside.

It was now 6pm, and I hadn't eaten since Bristol, not having moved away from the gate since I got back, the feel of the money coming my way getting the better of thoughts of food and drink.

But now I felt like I needed a rest, knew I would be doing the right thing stopping and sitting down for a decent meal. I had £450 in my money-belt plus about £30 in my pocket, but, although I had done well to get that amount, it didn't feel like I was doing as well as before I'd been captured by Alex.

The thought of Alex and the previous night made me put a hand on my abdomen, just to make sure the money-belt was still there. It was, and I felt for the pens, the one I had been using, which was in my pocket, and the other two that I'd stashed in the zip compartment of my rucksack. Everything was where it was the last time I checked a few minutes previously, and I suspected that fatigue was beginning to affect my ability to think straight. What I did know, though, was that once I had eaten I would get back to Billy and the camp and give the money I was carrying to H to look after.

I picked up the buzz of the place just walking down from Gate 2 towards the festival. Rather pointlessly, I looked over in the direction of where, after my escape the previous evening, I had stopped by the embers of a fire to get warm and have a smoke to see if I could locate the exact spot. There was no chance.

The field I was looking at had thousands of tents in it, many more than I had presumed were there when I'd taken advantage of the fire, and, even though I had been sitting quite close to the path, I couldn't work out where it had been. It didn't matter, but the sight of the field full of tents, a scene that indicated a packed house was, nonetheless, impressive.

The festival was jumping inside, and, as I walked down towards Babylon, the drag was packed with people coming from seeing a band in one field to watch another somewhere else. The stalls were busy as well, the traders appearing to be getting good value for the price they'd paid for their pitches.

From my right, I could hear the sound of Australian band Midnight Oil, who were performing on the Pyramid Stage, playing tracks from their recently released album *Earth And Sun And Moon*. Judging by the roar of the crowd, they were going down a storm. Next on the bill were The Velvet Underground, and, because of the amount of people walking the main drag towards the Pyramid Stage to watch them, it took me twenty minutes to reach the drag that would take me up towards the Green Fields. Once I had arrived, and after finding a suitable place to eat, I stopped, ordered a meal and spent about half an hour there, taking my time and chewing each mouthful of the main course properly before enjoying every lick, suck and bite of the two ice creams I had bought.

Once I had finished eating, the spliff that followed along with a cup of tea, made me feel satisfied and comfortable. I could have stayed there all night, drinking tea and smoking and watching the world contained within the Glastonbury Festival boundaries pass me by. But then, with my mind again returning to Alex and his crew, Billy, H, Gruff, my money and everything else, I turned away from the pleasant state of mind that I was slipping into and told myself to concentrate on the next and immediate task ahead, which was getting back to the camp.

The walk lasted about thirty minutes, what with me taking my time and not charging ahead in case I ran into the baddies. In addition, my brain was sending messages to my legs, telling them to save the newfound energy the food and sit-down had given them for later. And so it was 7.30pm when I reached the camp safely without seeing any of my potential predators.

As I approached our enclave, it struck me how quiet, still and peaceful it was away from the hustle and bustle of the festival. Even though there was the sound of a stereo playing somewhere, it was a distance away, and while the music of Eddie Reader in the Acoustic Tent reached me when the wind blew, the sound of birds singing their goodnight calls and the calm aura of the locality made this a brilliant place to camp.

Billy was lying on his sleeping bag outside his tent.

'Where the fuck have you been?' he said, the tone of his voice indicating he was somewhat surprised to see me.

I ignored the welcome and headed straight to my tent, went inside and shut the flap. I opened my main kitbag where I had stashed my money earlier in the morning and felt for the wad of notes. Yes, it was still there, and everything else seemed to be in the right place as well. As I breathed a sigh of relief, a real deep one, a full intake of air followed by a slow, thoughtful exhalation, I heard the sound of my tent being opened. It was Billy. Laughing this time, and with the slightest hint of concern as well as being just plain nosy, he asked again.

'Ho, big man, c'mon, where the fuck have you been?'

'How's it you lost your pen,' I asked, remembering earlier that morning when he couldn't be bothered waking up. 'I could have done with that.'

'Fuck knows what I done with it,' he answered, shaking his head and smiling. 'I was tripping off my nut.'

'Not done any graft then?'

'I couldn't, could I? I didna have a pen. Why, have you?'

Turning away, I felt inside my jeans and opened the zipper of my money-belt and took out all the money and peeled off £50. Keeping my back to him, I put the remaining £400 I had earned during the day in the plastic bag containing the cash I'd put away in the morning and hid it beneath my sleeping bag. Turning back to Billy, I gave him the £50.

'Done well then,' he responded. 'Thanks for that.'

'H or Gruff here?'

'No, they've gone to see some mad band or other, but Samantha and Joanna are. They're in the van with their boyfriends. Right, that's that. Now,' he continued, his expression turning to a grin, 'what the fuck have you been at all day? You've been up to something, I can tell.'

'Listen, Billy,' I replied quickly, wanting to put my stash of money with the rest that H was looking after, 'I'll tell you in a minute. Just let me have a wash and sort myself out, and I'll tell you what happened. Any chance of skinning me one up?'

Ordinarily, he would have made the excuse that it was my turn to do the honours, but the £50 I had just presented him with swayed the issue, and he retreated from my tent to his to find his puff and lick one dry for me.

As soon as Billy had gone, I reached for the money I'd concealed from him, and, hiding it by way of stuffing it down the front of my jeans, I went to the van to speak to the girls. As I got nearer, I could hear the sound of laughter. Opening the back door, I said my hellos and climbed inside. Joanna and Samantha had taken advantage of the fact that Gruff and H had left them in the van while they'd gone down to watch the band, and the two girls and their boyfriends were making the most of the comfortable mattresses and sleeping bags covering the otherwise cold metal floor.

'Not going out then?' I asked to none of them in particular as I sat in and shut the door, the two couples leaning against opposite sides of the van and facing each other.

'No,' replied Sam, laughing as she took a swig from a can of cider and laughing again as she looked at Joanna. 'We've had a great day already.'

'H not about?' I asked, even though Billy had already told me she wasn't.

'They've gone to see The Velvet Underground, and they're staying out to go and watch Suede, but they'll be back after that,' Joanna said, putting her hand in front of her mouth to try to stop herself laughing any more, but instead giggling, Samantha responding in kind.

'Are you lot waiting up for them?' I asked, realising I had entered something of a madhouse, the two girls struggling to avoid spilling their drinks as they rolled about, creasing up in fits of laughter. 'Can I leave something with you to give to H?'

There was nothing funny in what I'd said, but it only caused them to descend into more fits of laughter. Despite their jocular display, I managed to ascertain that they would 100 per cent definitely and without doubt be staying put and stashing my bag of money under what looked like some of H's kit. I moved towards the back of the van to leave.

'Joe,' said Samantha, wide eyed and trying to look serious but unable to, the ends of her lips turning ever so slightly upwards before her mouth became a smile, 'have you got any blow we could have? Billy gave us some earlier, but we've smoked it all.'

I started laughing now, realising why the two girls were in such a state. Feeling inside my jeans pocket, I found the lump of hash I had been carrying with me and passed it to Samantha, said cheerio and stepped out of the back of the van and slammed the door shut. I had left them with the rest of the eighth I'd started the day with, but it didn't bother me. I had plenty more. They were doing me a favour and were a decent couple of girls, as were the guys they were with. As well as that, I felt that it was helping me keep on the right side of the karma.

Walking away, I heard shrieks coming from inside the van and the sound of what must have been Joanna hitting the palm of her hand against the side of the Transit as her laughing fit got worse.

Fuck, I thought to myself. I hope they're not laughing at me.

The vision I had of them stoned had me chuckling when I reached my tent, and I was still smiling as I gave myself a good all-over wash and changed my clothes, preparing for the rest of the evening and the night ahead.

Keeping the rucksack that I'd been carrying containing the changes of clothes, I made sure that I left one of the two spare pens I had in the tent where I'd previously left my money, in case I lost the one I'd been using throughout the day, the other one in my bag as a spare for the evening. I also put on a different jacket from the one I'd been wearing when I was taken prisoner by Alex, choosing to take the parka that I wore when I was working as a builder's labourer.

Tomorrow was Saturday, the last day the stamp would be worth anything. That was because Sundays at Glastonbury were always then regarded as a free day, and at around about 11am the stewards manning the gates would disappear from their posts, leaving the festival open to all who wanted to come and go. If the worst did come to the worst, and I managed to lose both pens I was taking out that night, I would still have one back at base to see me through Saturday without having to go through the hassle of making another trip to Bristol to try to buy another.

Reloading, I made sure that I cut off a decent eighth from my personal, and, breaking it in half, put one piece in the fly pocket of my jeans and the other bit in my money-belt for safe-keeping, only to be used in an emergency situation. Double-checking that I had everything I could want for the night and possibly the next day, I satisfied myself that all was correct. Having done so, I stepped back out of my tent into the rapidly darkening evening, zipped the flap shut behind me and walked over to Billy, who was sitting in front of the spot where, last night, one of our lot had built a fire.

'You walking down?' I enquired as I held out my hand to take the smoke he offered me.

'Aye,' he said in the way he sometimes did, as if whatever it was he'd just said yes to would be a major effort. Half smiling, he stood to accompany me. 'Just as long, cuntybollocks,' he continued, exaggerating his Glaswegian drawl, 'you tell me just exactly what it is you've been up to.'

CHAPTER THIRTEEN

As I walked along with Billy, leaving our field and joining the lane that led down the hill towards Gate 3, I recounted only the most important details about what had happened when I ran into Alex and didn't tell him how much I'd made. He was my mate, and we always looked after each other when we got a few quid or a nice bit of puff, but I'd given him £50 of the money I had sweated for while he was out on the lash with Gerry, Sparky, Keyo, Davey B and whoever else was with them, probably spending a big chunk of the money he'd made from the stamp, and then, to top it all, he had lost his pen.

Over the years and on a scale of things, I had definitely done more for him than he'd done for me, or that was the way that I looked at it anyway, so, taking all things into consideration, the £50 that I'd dropped him earlier was a nice little bung for Billy. He had his puff, the others had whatever else he wanted and he had money for a beer and some scoff.

Concentrating on the details of my capture, the weapons used and the strength of numbers that comprised the enemy forces, I then went on to describe how I had been guarded the whole time, my escape and the journey to and from Bristol.

Compared with everyone else, I was quiet and kept myself to myself at home, knowing everybody but doing my own thing, and I definitely wasn't a full-time, seven-nights-a-week, on-the-town type of person like a lot of the others.

Don't get me wrong, I loved a good weekend out in the summer, starting on a Friday afternoon then on into the night, repeating the sequence on Saturday and then chilling in one of the several Sunday pubs that everyone used to drink in, finding out who got off with who, what crews were down from different parts of the country, who'd been arguing or fighting and who'd been nicked and for what, but that was enough for me. Unless one of the lads from out of town was down for a few days or there was something special on, Monday to Thursday was the time that I spent keeping my head down, out of the way and trying to do a little bit of this and that or whatever I had to do to earn a dollar.

Billy, on the other hand, was one of those guys who fitted in with everyone, got involved with everyone and was well known among those who'd come to live in the town from Scotland, the Midlands and the North of England. It could be a wild place sometimes, with groups of lads on holiday thinking they'd be coming down and finding a town full of carrot-crunchers whose women they'd shag as well as drinking their beer, but it wasn't like that. There were some pretty big firms hailing from the likes of Birmingham, Glasgow, Liverpool and Manchester, with all four cities seeing a regular flow of people travelling to and from the town. Other less glamorous and probably even grimmer northern cities were also represented, but not as strongly as the 'top four'. There was always a lot going on, and Devon and Cornwall Police were always on the trail of one, if not more, of the people Billy used to knock about with. Half the time he was only just managing to keep one step ahead of them himself.

Although Billy knew I could do a turn, that I knew the score about a few things, for me to get involved in what had happened over the last day or so was a side he'd never seen before, and he was somewhat taken aback. Considering I had surprised myself how I'd handled things, I suppose his reaction in itself wasn't unexpected, but as I continued the tale he seemed almost disbelieving, especially when I went into detail about how I'd first been mugged, before he then raised doubts about my inability to escape and the bottle I'd had to carry on working on my own. It didn't bother me that much. He could think what he wanted. After all, I had the money stashed away to prove it.

As we approached the top of the hill from which it would then be a downwards descent to the gate, there was a group of four – two couples – sitting on the left of the path. I looked at Billy, who knew what I was thinking, but his shrug of the shoulders in acknowledging the opportunity to earn a couple of quid was measured with a partial look of annoyance on his face. He was beginning to get on my nerves.

I walked over to where the four were sitting, asked the relevant questions and, as Billy came over, I introduced him as my business partner, and the deal was done. All four were stamped up at £10 per head, a nice £20 each for me and Billy for just walking the way we were going anyway. Lovely.

Just as we all stood to go to the gate, a girl who'd seen the transaction taking place and had guessed what was going on came running over to us.

'Can you get me and my friends in?' she asked eagerly, catching her breath after coming up the hill from the group of people at which she was pointing.

'How many of you are there?'

Before she had time to answer, Billy cut in, 'Fuck's sake!' he shouted. 'I cannae be bothered with all this now!'

'Hang on, Billy . . .'

'Na, fuck that!'

'Please,' said the girl, her right hand squeezing her left one in front of her thighs, knees buckling slightly and her head tilting a little to the right.

I looked back at the people I'd just stamped and then at Billy. The four that hoped they were coming in with us were looking gutted.

'Will you take them in?' I said, pointing my finger at the four. 'And you just keep the lot.'

Billy looked at the four, a sympathetic gene somewhere deep in his DNA kicking in, and replied, 'Aye, c'mon.'

With the smiles returned to their faces, the four stood ready to go. I looked at the girl.

'You ready?'

'Yeah,' she said, smiling, relieved that it looked like she and her friends would also now be getting in.

The four going with Billy had already started walking towards the gate as he passed in front of me. He didn't say anything. He didn't need to. I could see it on his face.

'You're a tit, you!' I hissed, the anger inside me threatening to burst out in far greater volume and violence than what had involuntarily spilled out of my mouth, my blood boiling over with sheer frustration.

'Prick!' he spat back at me as he increased his pace so as not to lose out on his four punters and the £40 he'd take from them once they were on the inside.

The girl started smiling. 'Good friend of yours then, is he?'

I let out a laugh and motioned her to lead the way to where her mates were. She said her name was Ruby and told me that there were seven of them altogether, including her, and they were all nurses who originally hailed from West London.

Three of them, including Ruby, had moved to Santa Monica, a plush district of California near Los Angeles, and had come back to the UK to meet up with their friends to travel together to the Glastonbury Festival. She explained that her four friends who still lived and worked in London had managed to wangle it so their shifts worked out that they were all off at the same time, and the seven of them had taken a chance and made their way to Somerset without tickets but were, nevertheless, hopeful of getting in.

I listened to her story for a few moments, and, after explaining that her friends who were employed by the NHS didn't have too much money to spend, she'd managed to charm me to the degree that I only charged £60 for everyone.

Taking Ruby and three others through first, it was noticeable how much more activity there was by the gate to the field we were walking through and on the lane immediately by the access point to Gate 3. As we got closer, the usual touting patter for entry to the festival became almost incessant, as did the offers for good clean pills and charlie.

Having briefed the girls not to bother, the four of us walked through, confident enough to ignore the offers of the sellers, but from what I picked up, albeit on that little stretch that was the hill down to the gate, the fact was there were loads of people now working the stamp, and the going rate to punters was £20 per head.

Although I had only been asking for £10, it was a price I'd set myself to charge because I realised that I wouldn't be the only one working the scam, and the usual undercutting competition rules of the street would apply. The way I looked at it was that for £10 per person everyone involved was doing the others a favour. Many of the people I'd taken through said they'd been asked if they wanted to get in by others, and that the price was £20 – and in some cases £25, according to one of Ruby's mates anyway – and what I'd learned from this impromptu market research was that everyone who had dealt with me was happy to risk a £10 note. I was happy, too.

Following what had happened to me on the Thursday night, my main concern was getting robbed or beaten up or both – or, even worse, getting caught by Alex again. The feel of the strap of my rucksack gave me reassurance – the knowledge that I had a change of clothing I'd already tested on that supervisor at Gate 2 earlier – as did the fact that I was wearing completely different clothes from those I'd had on when I was held prisoner by Alex's crew. As long as I kept the peak of my cap down low over my face, I was confident I wouldn't be spotted.

What did make things harder, though, was that, because most of the people working the gate were doing so with at least two or three others, they had the security of knowing that as well as them all watching out for each other they'd also have back-up if they got into trouble or were challenged by another firm. Because of this and because I was working alone, if I was going to do a bit I'd have no choice but to work the lanes a bit further away from the gate and away from the opposition.

I had intended to go into the festival to meet up with a few of those Billy had been with all that day. It was now Friday evening, and apart from the first day or so, and a few quick forays into the festival to grab some food or sleep, I hadn't seen some of the lads from home, any bands that were playing or any of the shows or done anything apart from stay near the gates and try to make money.

Usually, for me at least, going to Glastonbury, or indeed any festival, for a few days was my equivalent to a regular holiday such as a fortnight in Spain or Portugal. A festival was where I wanted to be to chill out and forget the worries of the everyday world. But this year, because of the stamp and the money I was making, it was different.

Crack on, I thought. Grab it while it's there.

What with walking Ruby and her friends through, going out again and up to their mates and then taking them in, I'd walked the crossroads on the lane some three times in about thirty minutes, and it gave me a good idea of who was doing what and where, and I recognised some of the people who had been grafting there since the Tuesday or the Wednesday.

In all probability, they, like the stewards, would see hundreds, if not thousands, of people walking by each hour, so it would be unusual to remember a face that had passed by innocently. But a person going past with regularity would more than likely draw their attention, bearing in mind that anyone doing something untoward like selling drugs usually acquires a natural paranoia and is constantly on the alert for rival gangs or the police.

Anyway, taking no chances, as I came out of the entry approach and back on to the lane after getting the last of Ruby's mates in, I turned to the left and walked up the path until it bent to the left and I could no longer see the lights from the entrance then waited next to a clearing in the shrubbery.

It was beginning to get dark and a bit eerie, and, although there were people constantly walking by, it wasn't as good a spot as it would have been during the day. Because of the fading light, people were wary of others approaching them, especially if they suddenly appeared out of the shadows. I felt alone and vulnerable, my heart always ready to beat a little faster and the butterflies in my stomach fluttering.

However, the longer I stayed where I was, the more familiar I became with the surroundings and felt increasingly comfortable as minutes turned into hours, but, what with the extra distance between the gate and where I was working, it started to tell on my legs and feet.

I had picked up a few punters and made another £130, getting a couple of twos, threes and a few singles in before I met a group of northern guys, fifteen in total, who, once one had come with me to make sure the stamp worked, agreed a fee of £120 for the lot as long as they saw themselves in.

After they'd headed off down the lane, I rolled a smoke and waited at least fifteen minutes to see if any of them came back because they had problems getting in. No one returned, and having been informed by one of the northerners that it was now 1.30am, and with the lanes still busy but the majority of people coming out, I decided to call it a night and headed for the camp. Without bothering to see who was awake, I went straight to my tent, got undressed and into my sleeping bag and crashed out.

That was how Friday night ended, and I slept soundly through until Saturday morning. As I opened my tent to survey the scene outside, there was a definite buzz in the air. Although it was only 8am, there were plenty of others in and around where we were camped, with Gruff, H, Samantha, Joanna and their boyfriends already up and enjoying breakfast, taking their time eating their muesli in the warm rays of a morning sun that dominated a clear sky. Others in the vicinity were doing likewise, the smell of sausages and bacon being grilled by someone close by drifting under my nose. As well as the sound of the BBC news coming from a vehicle parked nearby – it was that which had woken me up – others were listening to their choice of entertainment, with the strains of 'Twisting By The Pool' by Dire Straits coming from one direction and Pink Floyd's 'Shine On You Crazy Diamond' being blasted out from another.

I stepped out from my tent to stretch, the arms reaching upwards attracting the attention of Gruff and H.

'Joe! How ya doing?' enquired Gruff by way of a shout, causing Sam and Joanna to turn around and look at me which, in turn, caused them to start giggling. Remembering their fits of laughter from the previous evening, I shook my head in mock disgust and turned to H and Gruff.

'Good. How are you?'

Not bothering to wait for an answer, I then turned to H.

'Did the dynamic duo tell you I called last night?' I said, pointing my thumb backwards over my shoulder at Sam and Jo, the two of them laughing even louder as I spoke.

Tempted to join them, H maintained a straight face, although there was a slight crack of a smile on her lips.

'Yes, don't panic. I've put it with the rest.'

'Got some more for you. You two OK for money?'

She declined the offer. I handed H the cash I'd made the previous night, as Gruff turned his head and looked at me with a serious expression.

'You worry me you do.'

'Why's that then?'

'Bumped into Billy last night down by the main stage . . . He said you had some sort of trouble.'

'Oh yeah? Well, I don't look like I'm in any trouble now, do I?' I replied, my tone calming rather than reactive. 'And I haven't brought any trouble up here.'

Gruff looked at H and then back at me.

'How much have you got now?'

'Twenty-nine.'

'Twenty-nine? Two hundred and ninety?'

'Two thousand nine hundred,' I answered quietly.

As if shocked by my reply, his body slumped back into the camping chair he was sitting in before his head went forward, mouth half open in awe.

'Two thou –' he began.

'Shush,' I whispered, quickly but directly at him, indicating that a stranger from one of the surrounding tents and vans might hear.

'Two thousand nine hundred?' he said, this time getting it all out but in a hushed whisper.

'Yeah, but that's between me and you. I don't want anyone else finding out how much I've got,' my head turning in the direction of Billy's tent.

They nodded in agreement.

'Is that it then? Are you going to stop?'

I shook my head. 'I want the money . . .'

'Listen, Joe . . .' he started, before giving me a lecture about the dangers of Glastonbury, as well as beating the jungle drum himself about a rumour going around that two brothers had been battered somewhere, and that they'd both been stabbed and one had a fractured skull and broken jaw. It all sounded a little too convenient for my liking, with Gruff being prone to a bit of exaggerating when he was trying to get a point across. Not wanting to upset him, I listened quietly and let him finish having his say. He shook his head and looked at H, but she just smiled at me, looked back at Gruff and shrugged her shoulders.

'Be careful. Please stay out of trouble.'

'Yeah, no worries.'

I turned around to walk away, and both Sam and Jo had stopped laughing, serious expressions on their faces as they sat there at the table quietly listening to the conversation. Smiling, I produced a little lump of puff and placed it in front of them.

'You guys have a good day now,' I said, making their laughter return. Then, turning to the six of them, 'See you lot later.'

Going back to my tent, I considered looking in to see if Billy was back but decided against the idea, preferring to get my kit together for the coming day. After the completion of my washing routine, I dressed, packed my rucksack and pockets with everything I needed and walked off in the direction of Gate 3.

I don't know why, but I suddenly thought of trying somewhere that I hadn't yet been and changed direction, went to find the motorbike-taxi man. He was awake and had been up for ages on account of the sound system blasting out the Floyd was nearer to his camp than ours, but he joked about it, saying that he was a big fan so couldn't really complain. He was happy with the £10 I offered him for the lift and sold me a nice bit of polm – sometimes referred to as pollen – and promised to save me a bit for Sunday when I'd want some for the last day and to take home.

He gave me a lift around the lanes to the other side of the farmhouse, which, when not being used as the Glastonbury Festival HQ, was the hub of Worthy Farm and the home of Michael Eavis, and dropped me by Gate 1. This was at the top of a steep incline, overlooking the hill at the bottom of which was the main stage.

I had made up my mind to try Gate 4, which, from where we were camped, was at the other end of the festival behind the main stage. By getting dropped off here, I had saved myself a long walk to work. Now, instead of having to trek through the festival, queuing up at Gate 3 for the early-morning rush to get in and then facing a good twenty-five minute hike, I'd only have to cut across in front of the main stage to get to where I intended to graft.

There's never usually anything on at the main stage before about 11am, and the walk down through the tents pitched on the hill overlooking it was the hardest part, making sure that I didn't go flying by tripping over their guy ropes, but once I reached the flat where those standing to watch the gigs gather, the walk to Gate 4 only took a few minutes.

Although it could be used by ticket-holding festival-goers, Gate 4 was the entrance to and from the Stage Road. It was along there that the bands used to enter the festival on their tour buses along with the equipment. Gate 4 was also where lorries and vans delivering goods to the traders working the festival entered and exited. It was quite a busy place.

The approach to the gate was different from Gates 2 and 3 in that the area was flat and it was more of a road than a lane. That led directly to a gate that was closed to everything except vehicles entering and leaving the festival, and a road to the left that went up and around the perimeter all the way past where the fence curved to the right to keep intruders away from the farmhouse and the farm's outbuildings. Although the Stage Road was a thoroughfare for vehicles associated with the festival, people had parked their cars and set up camp right along the side of the road, and there were several fields that had been set aside to be used as camping areas and car parks.

Gates 2 and 3 were the ones through which the vast majority of those attending the festival went, but Gate 4 was still busy. Like the others, there were people hanging about near the gate offering their various services to the people passing by. Despite it being Saturday, the second day of the festival proper, people were still arriving, many travelling overnight to get there, and plenty were without tickets, having made an impulsive decision after seeing the event reported on the television news.

Unlike some festivals, where people can buy day tickets, the £58 that a ticket for Glastonbury cost that year was for the whole weekend, so the price of unauthorised entry would hold its value right up until Sunday when the gates were left open and unmanned. Anyone protesting that they were only there for the Saturday night was given short shrift by those working the entry scam, and, after a watch of and a listen to of a few of those who were getting others in, I established that the current going rate for either a fake stamp or a hole in the fence was in the region of £20 per person.

With the gate being used to allow vehicles entry and exit, there were a lot more stewards involved in policing the area. As a result, those offering a way in or selling their drugs were less conspicuous than they were at the other gates, which, in turn, resulted in this place being less wild than the others.

This had its advantages for me, an independent who was working alone and battling for business against others on the same scam but in numbers. The stewards would not and could not let a situation get too far out of control if it was taking place right in front of them, and they would be forced to step in, either dealing with it themselves or calling the police who were ever eager to show their presence. The downside was that the stewards and officials had a good view of the approaches to the gate and could monitor any activity taking place nearby. Despite that, many working scams were blatantly obvious, their bravado and brazen attitude grating at some of the onlooking officials. I again chose to work a good distance away from the gate, the flat path being easy to walk compared with the lanes by Gates 2 and 3, with none of the inclines or the hill to climb.

By about 10am I had taken nine people in, charging £15 per head, and I was coming back out having got the last couple through when I saw a couple of faces in a group of four people that I recognised from football. As I got closer, it became apparent they were touting tickets.

'I'll buy any spare tickets, tickets for sale! I'll buy or sell any spares!' shouted one, the patter that he used at football matches and concerts no different from the words he was using here. I approached the guy standing next to the one shouting.

'Alright, mate. I know you from Chelsea, don't I?'

He looked at me, his eyes studying my face, brain going into overdrive wondering who I was and what I was on.

'I was sitting right behind you at Sheffield United, the last game of the season.'

His mate looked at me and nodded in recognition. He let out a laugh.

'Fuck me! That was a day!' he exclaimed.

Chelsea had played Sheffield United away at Bramall Lane with many of the travelling supporters turning up in fancy dress. It was a good turn-out by those who'd made the journey from London, their efforts not matched by the players as Chelsea crashed 4-2 with David 'Rodney' Lee and Andy Townsend scoring for The Blues. The fancy dress and fanatical Chelsea support apart, the game was memorable for the fact that it was caretaker manager David Webb's last match in charge having taken over the previous February and guiding the side away from relegation.

'I remember now,' said the first guy. 'You and your mates were the ones smoking the funny cigarettes.'

I started laughing.

'You're not in the drug squad are you, mate?' I asked, a charge which he strenuously denied. 'Top support that day, mate, weren't it?' I continued. 'You get back alright?'

There had been a bit of trouble after the match, with quite a few people from London getting involved, some having to drive home with dents in their motors and replacement windscreens, and, from what I remembered about seeing the guy at the game, he and his mates had gone by car. It turned out he hadn't had any hassle after the match, and he and those with him had an uneventful journey back to the capital. Once the football chatter was exhausted, he asked me what I was doing and whether I wanted a ticket.

'I'm working it myself,' I said, and because he and the other guys I had spoken to were Chelsea supporters, which meant, in theory, that we would all stick together, I then went on to give them an account of getting turned over by 'a bunch of fucking yardies' and my subsequent ordeal and escape.

Having listened to me, they agreed that I could work with them, helping to push the tickets they were selling while they minded me in return for a fiver of the £20 fee I would now be charging for the stamp. That suited me fine, and, with the security of having the back-up I'd needed the previous day, I stood with them and went about my business.

They – Herbie, Chris, Mark and Paul – had only arrived at Glastonbury that morning and cursed the fact they hadn't turned up on the Friday. The tickets for the festival had sold out in advance, and they would have made a fortune, but, as it was, they were paying fifteens and no more than twenty when they were buying and selling for nothing less than face value and once or twice getting £70.

I'd done OK, taking eleven in after persuading them to walk away and out of sight of the gate so I could stamp them up, earning £220, £55 of which went to Herbie and the others. The remaining £165, together with the £145 I had made before I met them, meant a nice £310, all of it safely in my money-belt, less a tenner I'd use for food and a drink.

The proximity of the area I was working, however, meant that the frequency with which I was going in and out of the festival had increased, and the changes of shirts and hats that were in my rucksack were proving handy. To ensure I wouldn't be spotted by any of the gate stewards, I got into the habit of changing my shirt every time I'd gone through and, before returning back out, changing it again.

What I couldn't quite work out was why people would want to pay full price for a ticket when there were cheaper ways of getting in. At the same time, I wondered why those who'd sold their tickets so cheaply hadn't just connected with those who were willing to stump up the full value. It was a funny old world, and it takes all sorts to make it, especially the world that was the Glastonbury Festival, but analysing the thought processes of the people buying the tickets was beginning to mash my brain. I needed a rest.

Telling the others that I was going for a break, I walked back through the gate just as a new shift of security staff was coming on duty. As they went to their allocated positions, one caught my eye. It was Pat D, one of the hundreds of lads from Glasgow who'd made Devon their home, and he was a familiar face to many. He was a good guy, and we knew each other well, our paths having crossed many times over the years.

At night he was a bouncer and used to work a couple of pubs midweek before doing the door at the main club that all the lads used to use at the weekend. His presence on the door came in handy when there was a queue and for paying nothing to get in, Pat backing their stories that those on free entry were local hotel or club staff.

He told me that he'd got a job with the security firm by chance and that the money he was on for working Glastonbury was good. He was doing an eight-hour shift each day from the Tuesday morning before the festival and working right through until the Tuesday after it finished. He would be at Gate 4 for each of his shifts.

Pat said that the previous evening he'd met Billy, Gerry and the rest of the lads where they gathered every year to watch the bands playing the main stage, and he'd stood with them and watched The Velvet Underground and Robert Plant but left half-way through The Black Crowes. He also told me that Billy had told him about the stamp and me getting kidnapped.

Pat was good enough to say that if I got myself in any more bother I should come and give him a shout if any of the others weren't about, and he'd make sure that when I started working the stamp again he'd try to see to it that I didn't get any hassle from the stewards.

Before we could chat further, he got a tap on the shoulder from one of his colleagues to tell him that he was wanted by his supervisor for something, and we shook hands. I carried on and into the festival for a sit-down, some food and drink and a nice fat joint. I found somewhere to eat that had chairs and tables, taking my time eating, and contemplated the way people bumped into each other in the least likely of places, as had happened with me meeting Pat and, to a certain extent, the touts from Chelsea.

The thought of them set off the trigger in my brain to yet again calculate the money I had earned. With the £300 I had on me and what was safely with H, I'd amassed £3,200 – £200 over my target – but the lust for more got the better of me as I considered the possibility of another £300 so that I'd have a nice round £3,500 to take home.

The way my mind was working, that calculation had a flaw in it, as if I were to take that amount home I'd need to earn another ton at least, maybe £150, to leave me with some money to spend on the Sunday, the day that the stamp was no longer required and a day I could spend chilling out.

There again, if I could get the three plus the expenses I wanted, what was to stop me getting four? Four plus the extra even? It was only 11.30am, and it wouldn't be dark until about 9.30 at night, and if I worked real hard and got ten people in an hour for ten hours that would be one thou . . . I stopped myself from thinking of the figure, my expectations suddenly measured by the very real knowledge that something might go wrong, the thought causing the butterflies in the pit of my stomach to flutter yet again. It was time to go, time to stop dreaming and start working, and, whatever I earned from now until the end, would be great, just great.

As I passed through the barriers and collected my stamp from the steward, I saw Pat who returned my smile with a sly wink. There was no need for him to let anyone he was working with know that he knew me.

Walking out, I looked for Herbie, Mark and the other two but couldn't see them. I took the road to my right, just in case they'd moved away from the gate to do a bit of trade. I'd gone a couple of hundred yards or so up the lane, and, as I passed by a van and some parked cars, I saw Mark and Herbie's backs behind a motor set a little bit back from the rest, so I cut between the gaps of the motors in front of it to make my way to them.

The two had their backs to the lane and were leaning against a car, and I could just see the top of the heads of the other two, with Herbie looking as though he was in deep conversation with someone. As I came into the space they were occupying, I noticed that there were a dozen or so others with them, all black. As Mark greeted me with an 'Oi, oi,' the guy that Herbie was speaking to looked up, and our eyes met. It was Alex.

CHAPTER FOURTEEN

As Alex looked at me in disbelief, then at Herbie, and then at me again, I instinctively took a step back. Grabbing a baseball bat that was resting, handle up, against his legs, he pushed himself off the car he'd been leaning against, and, glancing at Herbie, screamed, 'Him?'

With his boys now all standing, and Herbie and his three following suit but backing away, Alex smashed his bat against the car, shattering the rear indicator light and creasing its chrome surround, and made a move towards me. As I took another step back, I could see his lads making their way between the cars either side of me to try to get around the back and prevent me getting away. To my right, Carlton was swinging his bat around his head, keeping it under control with the rope loop that went through the handle, the glint in his eye and the sneer on his face telling me that he thought the time had come for him to do the business. Although I knew that there was nowhere to run, I kept on retreating with Alex coming for me square on.

'You tellin' people we're a bunch of yardies!' he shouted, inflicting a dent on the car he was now passing to try to get to me.

'You were fucking acting it!' I responded, my reply prompting another smash of the bat to the car.

Alex was still walking towards me, and I saw Herbie and his mates cower as the dull sound of wood on metal rang out again. He was within about fifteen feet, and, with his boys now behind me, any chance of escape had been cut off. Alex looked at Herbie as I narrowed my shoulders, trying to slip the rucksack off my back so I could use it to cover my head when the beating started, but I stumbled, what with walking backwards, and the straps rode back up my arms as I put them out to steady myself. Alex was getting nearer.

'And you told them that you'd earned me over £1,100, and I only gave you £40?' his voice angry but controlled, his arm raised as if to bring the bat down on the car for a third time.

'It's true. I was counting!' I shouted back at him.

My response stopped Alex and all those with him in their tracks. He looked embarrassed and lowered his eyes, while the others turned their stares away from me and on to him, the angry, hate-filled expressions on their faces having changed to looks of doubt, which were directed towards their leader as they considered what I'd said.

Keeping my eyes focused on Alex, I took another step back as everyone else kept their eyes on him. Suddenly, their attention was taken by the sound of smashing glass and three or four people arguing. It was coming from the other side of the lane where an ice-cream van was parked and in front of which some of those passing had begun to gather.

For a moment everything and everyone seemed to stand still – until I felt the hand of someone behind me grabbing my collar, the grip on my shirt doubling as a fist was pressed into my neck, pushing my head downwards. Despite the hold, I managed to twist enough to see Alex's face, his evil eyes focusing on me, probably considering my fate, but, as I started to think that my luck might have run out, he shook his head slowly and indicated that whoever had hold of me should bring me with him as he led the way out from among the cars and on to the drag to see exactly what the commotion was about. The one holding me lowered his hands as he was joined by Carlton and Duane, who, saying nothing, both gave me a real deep look that said they'd only need the slightest of excuses.

Together with my three-man escort, we joined the rest of Alex's crew on the drag. There were twelve of them in total, all standing across the road, abreast of each other in a semi-circle, watching the proceedings taking place in front of the ice-cream van. As I stood on the left end of the line, I looked to my right where I could see Herbie talking to Alex, who, as he listened, kept glancing at me.

'You robbing cunts!' shouted an agitated guy in his thirties, his venom directed at a couple of travellers who looked like they were squaring up to have a go at him.

In his hand he had a £20 note that he was waving at them and holding aloft for all who were there to see.

'Fucking trying to turn me over with this shit?' he ranted, as he approached the pair.

Although he was carrying quite a large knife in his other hand, the two he was challenging were holding their ground, and, even though it was still at the handbags stage, the incident seemed as if it might become gravely serious as one of the two travellers pulled a nunchaku from inside his shirt. As he started to swing it, going forward towards the guy with the knife, someone who had been watching went running off in the direction of the gate.

It sounded as if the owner of the ice-cream van had been chosen by the two travellers as a suitable recipient for a dodgy £20 note. Obviously perturbed at being taken for a mug, he'd picked up the knife and jumped out of the back of his van to confront the perpetrators, but in doing so had left the back door open. As he moved further away from the van, he left the perfect opportunity for any sneak-thief who happened to be passing to get inside and steal his takings.

I was standing about twenty yards away, and as the distance between its open door and the man grew wider I took a step towards the back of the van. As I moved, I felt a rush of air as Carlton came close to connecting his bat with my head, the side of it brushing my scalp, but as I cowered I turned and pointed at the open door and half whispered, 'Rob the till!'

Stealing the ice-cream-man's money was the last thing I wanted to do, but, with the prospect of being battered by Alex and his mates, I thought I'd try to kid them into thinking I might be of some use, and, in an attempt to ingratiate myself with them, albeit for the purposes of self-preservation, I continued with my pretence.

Duane gave Carlton a nod as they let me off their leash, and I started to take a few careful steps further towards the van. Exaggerating the persona I had suddenly acquired, I ensured that everyone who had their eyes on me saw me giving the passers-by who'd stopped to watch the incident a proper once-over to ensure they hadn't seen me making my move towards the open door.

Fortunately for both my conscience and the ice-cream man, the sight of a Land Rover full of stewards emerging from inside the security cordon at the gate and turning right up the lane in our direction put an end to my charade, and Alex gave the signal to his troops to withdraw. With Duane grabbing me by my rucksack, he and Carlton bundled me up the lane, and the rest of the crew followed, leaving Alex talking to Herbie and Chris.

We'd gone about fifty yards when we stopped and turned to see what was happening back down the road. The Land Rover had now come to a halt beside the ice-cream van, and it looked like the stewards had detained the two travellers and were starting to give them a grilling. With the incident being dealt with, we continued walking up the lane for several minutes before we turned off and into the field on the left. Going first through the lines of parked cars, we then weaved through the tents and encampments beyond until we reached a green plastic tarpaulin suspended between the roofs of two Transit minibuses.

There, sitting in the deck chairs underneath the cover, were three black girls and some guys in the immediate vicinity, a couple lying on a duvet in front of a tent and another sitting at a plastic camping table and building a joint. As I surveyed the scene, I felt an arm come around my back and a hand squeeze my shoulder. It was Alex.

'A word . . .' he said, as he pulled me in towards the side of one of the minibuses, turning me around so I had my back to everyone else.

'Where my £40?'

'What?'

'That money I was good enough to give you.'

I sighed, dropped my head and leaned against the Transit.

'Looks like you're working for me again, Chelsea boy . . .'

I looked at him as if to say, *How did you know that?* and at the same time realised that Herbie must have told him. Alex continued, 'I know your friend Herbie like I know a lot of people, and it's lucky for you that I do.'

'Yeah?'

'He's had a word on your behalf, that is after he told me about his mate from Chelsea being turned over by a . . . by a bunch of yardies, I do believe. Now, where's my money?'

Ignoring his request for a refund, I stared straight at him, holding his gaze.

'You into football then?'

'Yeah, I'm into football,' he said confidently, smiling as he did so.

'Who do you support then?'

He looked back at me, still smiling, and with an air of defiance answered, 'Millwall, and I'm a top supporter . . . My money!'

Before I had time to react, he'd spun me around, nodded his head at Carlton and Duane and left them to pat me down, the pair of them splitting the money they took from the pockets of my Levi's and putting it in with their own, Carlton taking care of all the coins himself while the younger members of the firm watched on, their eyes wide, learning the rules of engagement ready for the time when it would be their turn to mimic the actions of their peers. My jacket pockets and bag were next, with Duane already having taken the pen I was using from my jeans before discovering the spare, but again, and to my relief, they missed my money-belt.

Once they'd finished rifling my pockets and examining the contents of the bag, Carlton held it up as if to show it to Alex and called him over. Alex looked at it and opened his mouth to say something, but I cut in. I didn't want to lose it or the shirts and caps it contained.

'I'll need that if I'm working for you.'

'And how's that?'

'It's my change of clothes for going in and out. I change every time I go through the gate so I don't get spotted by the stewards.'

Alex, his eyes studying me intently and his head nodding slightly in my direction, said to Carlton, 'Let him keep it.'

Handing it back, he indicated to me that I should move away from where I was standing, and he pointed to a car and told me to wait there. As I leaned against its doors, a couple of girls sauntered over to join the company, and one of them, looking surprised to see me in the middle of their group, looked right down her nose at me before sneering, 'What's *he* doing here?' loudly to nobody in particular but so everybody could hear.

I looked her in the eyes.

'What's that then? 'Cos I'm white?'

She glared back and right through me. Everybody was looking at me, and they all heard this bit of banter. I stood there, surrounded by cars and the firm of the bruvvas, not quite sure what would happen next. Two young guys then approached me, obviously sent over by Alex to keep a watch on my movements or, rather, make sure I didn't go too far.

'And what do you do with your time then?' said one.

I looked at them both.

'I'm a Chelsea supporter.'

'Oh yeah?' he said. 'Isn't that a racist team?'

'What, just like your girlfriend over there you mean?' I said, pointing to the girl.

That cut the conversation stone dead, and I was well happy. In my mind, I'd shut them out of my thoughts and searched for and found a diversion. Somewhat surprisingly, but for the second time, when I was turned over and frisked my puff wasn't taken from me, and I got out my stash and asked the two watching over me for permission to make a spliff. They agreed, and I duly rolled a joint and lit it. Looking at another girl who was in the company and motioning to the car that I assumed belonged to one or other of her number, I said, 'OK if I sit in and smoke this?'

'Help yourself,' she replied.

I pulled on the door handle only to find that it was locked. This brought hysterical shrieks of laughter from the girl and her mates, and I realised that the car belonged to no one there. I saw the funny side of it as well and started to laugh. This seemed to break the ice, and I sat down on the grass and smoked my joint.

With the sun overhead, its midday rays beating down and causing the temperature to rise to uncomfortable levels, which suitably matched my concerns for my safety, I sat quietly right in the heart of this crew, watching all the activity going on around me and contemplating my fate and wondering how I was going to get away.

Over the course of the next half an hour or so, and in threes and fours, more people joined the group, stayed for a few minutes and then left, and I estimated that there must have been at least forty or fifty in total. They were all black and most were males, with several looking as if they were sixteen or seventeen years old, while the majority appeared as if they were in their mid-twenties with Alex probably in his mid-thirties. There were twelve or so girls in the company, including the one who had taken a pop at me and the couple who were laughing at me, so, all in all, it was a right old firm.

Listening to them talking, it was obvious they were at Glastonbury for one purpose and for one purpose only, and that was to make money. Alex looked like he was someone they all showed respect to. He seemed to be in charge of operations, as a succession of the younger members of the crew presented themselves and handed money to him before talking to one of his lieutenants, who then passed them clear plastic bags of what I suspected were either Es or wraps of cocaine.

Whatever they were up to, they were busy, but, although what they were doing was patently illegal and they'd naturally be on their toes anyway, there was a certain nervousness about Alex, Duane, Carlton and a couple of the others I'd been with on the Thursday evening. They hadn't showed this at the time, and I couldn't work out the reason why.

Alex puzzled me as well, especially what he'd said about being a Millwall supporter. I didn't know too much about who was doing what in the various firms that made up the Bermondsey side's hooligan element, but the only black person I knew of from any of their lot was someone called Tiny, who'd been around in the '70s and '80s, and Alex looked like he was too young to have been him.

By now, I didn't doubt that he and a good few of the lot with him at Glastonbury were from south London, their accents contrasting with a few of the others whose dialect was interspersed with what sounded like traces of Bristolian and Mancunian, but they didn't matter. The chances were that if Alex was a Millwall supporter, he probably lived somewhere in deepest, darkest New Cross, Peckham or Lewisham, where the gang culture of the local youth was beginning to make its mark. The tools they were carrying and the way they were behaving fitted the description – the gun, bats and knives I had seen probably not the only weapons in their possession. If it did finally come to the point when I was going to get done over, this lot wouldn't fuck about.

With all the different people who were coming and going, I hardly took any notice of one of the younger members of the crew, who, after emerging from the mass of tents and cars we were pitched up by, reported straight to Alex. He had, up until that point, been sitting in one of the camping chairs surveying the scene, the lord of his very own manor. After a few moments of intense conversation, with Duane and Carlton called over to listen, Alex stood, a look of concern on his face, as Carlton and Duane whispered hushed instructions to their foot soldiers who, as they received their orders, also began to mobilise.

'All my lot, come with me,' said Alex, his voice exuding authority and making everyone take notice.

With fifteen trailing him plus me and three new minders, he led the way through the parked cars and along the side of the lane and back down the rise towards Gate 4.

Staying on the right-hand side, we stopped by the road opposite the gate, but just far enough away so we were out of the immediate sight-line of the stewards. There were still plenty of newcomers arriving, and, within a couple of minutes, I was working again, shepherding four in for £80 with the three that Alex had assigned to look after me also in tow. We joined the queue to get in with two of Alex's boys at the front, one at the back and me in the middle, the punters in pairs either side of me. As we waited in line, I saw Pat watching the ranks of people waiting their turn to get through the gate. Our eyes met, but before he could return my look with one of recognition, I'd touched each of my eyes with my forefingers and then crossed them in front of my face – a bit of tic-tac that he knew meant danger – and he began to make his way over to the point at which I'd have my ultraviolet stamp checked.

I glanced at the minder behind me, who was watching to make sure I wasn't going to mess him about, turned away and gave a broad smile to a couple we were taking in. As our turn to get through came closer, I leaned forward putting my mouth close to the ear of the punter in front and whispered, 'You OK?' She returned an affirmative smile just as the lead escort looked back from the front to check his cargo was still OK, but although his eyes were on the line I had the feeling he was avoiding the gaze of the stewards rather than making sure we were still there.

With the stewards working quickly, it wasn't long before it was my turn to show them my stamp. As I stepped forward and offered my arm for inspection, I looked behind to ensure the tail-end Charlie had his view obscured by those in front of him and, confident he wouldn't notice, I slipped my hands inside the front of my Levi's, opened my money-belt and wrapped my right hand firmly around the bundle that was my £300 and held it in my fist. By the time I'd been given the nod to proceed, what with my stamp having been approved, Pat was standing at the side of the barriers just past where the stewards were checking entry, and as I walked past he stopped me.

'Excuse me, sir, can I recheck your stamp please?'

Turning, I could see that the minder at the end had held back, and as we both looked at each other I shrugged my shoulders, feigning innocence, and held my arm out for Pat so that he could check my stamp.

As he held my left wrist in his left hand, I passed Pat the wad of money and whispered, 'Grab this. There's three there. Keep fifty for yourself, and I'll see you soon . . .'

He gave me a look of acknowledgement, but, continuing the charade of my behalf, he said, 'OK, pal, your stamp looks fine, enjoy the day.'

'Cheers,' I replied, and, safe with the thought that I had nothing on me for them to steal, I continued towards the two who had led the punters through the gate and waited for those behind me.

Once their money had been collected, my escort and I made our way back through the exit gate and headed back to where we had left Alex and his crew. As we went past a group of stewards, I could see Pat among them, and, as our eyes met, he gave me a wink as if to say he was watching my back, that the money I'd given him to look after would be there for me whenever I caught up with him.

We got back to where the others were waiting, and, for a few moments, I sat on the grass and watched as my minders passed Alex the money we'd taken. After a few moments' consideration and following a conversation with one of his boys, Alex decided that we would move away from Gate 4 and go up towards Gate 1, an entry point on the brow of the hill that overlooked the main festival entrance.

Standing up, I exposed my now empty money-belt that had somehow ridden up my abdomen and was around my waist. I glanced to see if anyone had noticed. Duane had seen it, and, although I knew he'd taken a mental note that I had it about my person, for some reason he didn't bother taking the time to see what was inside.

It took us half an hour to make our way to Gate 1, up the lanes and around the outside of the perimeter fence, and, in the heat of the day and walking uphill most of the way, by the time we reached our destination the majority of our party were only fit to sit on the grass at the edge of the path and recuperate.

The track leading from the main festival entrance to Gate 1 was on a hill with a good view from the top of all those making their way up the slope towards the entry point. There were cars and vans parked up on both sides of the track, the majority facing in the direction of the entry gate, as if they were somehow marking the path that the new arrivals should follow. At the bottom and to the left was the main entrance from the road that came in from the direction of the M5 motorway, and even from our considerable distance it was a hive of activity.

There was a constant stream of people both walking to and away from the festival, with a fair proportion being latecomers, who would only enjoy one night at Glastonbury, making the journey up the hill towards the entry gate. Of those arriving, there were plenty who had turned up without tickets, and business was brisk.

We had plotted up about sixty or seventy yards down from the gate on the left-hand side of the verge, with Alex and his lads chilling while I grafted, my captors only stirring when I had some business. We'd been there for at least an hour, and, by this time, I was talking to the punters and arranging the deals myself with the crew just getting involved when it came to looking after the ultra-violet pen, taking the people in and collecting the money.

My sales pitch changed in that I was telling those who wanted a stamp that, if they slipped me a drink, I would tell my minders I'd negotiated a special rate. Even though there was less than a night and day's worth of festival left, all those I took in were more than happy with me charging them £25 each, £20 of which went to Alex while I took a fiver for myself.

We were away from the direct sight of the stewards manning the gate, but I wasn't happy working so close to it and suggested to Alex that it might be better if I was to move a bit further away. He was happy with this and gave his OK, motioned to two of his lads – Tony and Lewis – to go with me, and the three of us walked a little further down the slope, and I began to tout for business.

CHAPTER FIFTEEN

The afternoon sun was shining down from a clear blue sky, making it another iconic summer's day. The strains of Alison Moyet, who was performing on the Pyramid Stage, were reaching us, and there was an air of calm and a positive vibe emanating from the festival. As we walked away from Alex and his crew, I turned to Tony.

'It's great here, isn't it?'

He smiled, as did Lewis, and they both nodded in agreement.

'Spliff?' I enquired.

'We're OK,' Tony replied, 'but feel free to have one yourself – we could do with a sit-down anyway.'

We stopped, and as I started to roll a joint the subject of conversation turned to Glastonbury and what Tony and Lewis and the rest of their lot thought about the festival, and, almost inevitably, the name of Alex came up.

'To be honest,' said Tony, 'me and Lewis think he's a wanker – it's just one of those things that, while we're here, we're wrapped up with him. He's a bully with a bunch of idiots latching on to him. We wouldn't be doing this if we were here on our own.'

What Tony said surprised me. It was the first bit of humanity that any of Alex's crew had shown towards me, and it was welcome. Rather than pursue that part of the conversation, I turned it to where they came from, and, as I had suspected, they were from south London but were with people from all over the country, including Manchester and Bristol.

In complete contrast to Alex, Carlton and Duane, Lewis and Tony seemed like decent people. They were in their mid-twenties, and, although definitely streetwise, they didn't act like they wanted to be gangsters. They were just an ordinary couple of guys with none of the traits of the three who'd mugged me. They'd both told me they weren't impressed by Alex and wished they weren't with him, and I believed them.

It was the first time they'd been to Glastonbury, and they told me that they loved it and reiterated the fact that it would have been better if they weren't involved in what they were doing. However, it turned out that they were cousins, and the main reason they were at the festival with Alex was to try to earn some cash. Between them, they explained that Tony's sister had a five-year-old boy who needed to go to the USA for surgery to be treated for quadriplegia, a type of cerebral palsy that meant he couldn't use his legs properly. Tony and Lewis – together with the rest of their family – were desperately trying to get the money necessary to send the child to America in order that the operation could take place. After eighteen months of sponsored walks and similar fund-raising activities, they were now just a couple of thousand pounds short of their target. It was a heart-rending tale.

Their story told, the discussion again turned to Glastonbury, and they both said that they'd be back for the next festival, but they would come on their own to enjoy it and not to graft. I made up my mind that, despite the bravado and the front they were putting on in front of Alex, underneath it all, these two were alright. After about ten minutes' pleasant chat, we stood to go about our business.

As we headed down the path a Transit van pulled up right next to where we were walking, the passenger door opening as it slid to a halt.

'Alright, Joe! Can you get us in?'

It was Shieldsy, a mate of mine, who, although he was from Liverpool, I had met when he and loads of his mates had moved from the Northwest to the south coast. Shieldsy was one of the main faces living in a Dorset town in an area known as The Triangle, and he had arrived at Glastonbury with ten others including Newt, Twegs, Jordo and Willo, who also resided in the same area.

'Oi, oi, Jim,' I replied, calling him by his Christian name, momentarily forgetting Tony was there, pleased to see a few of my mates from way back, people I hadn't seen for years. 'Yeah, no problem, mate, you're all in.'

I went over to shake their hands as Tony and Lewis stood watching. Shieldsy and Jordo stopped and looked at them, saying nothing but with their faces speaking for them.

'These are my mates,' I said, letting the Scousers know that they best save whatever they were thinking for another time. 'We're working together.'

'Can you get us in, Joe?' Jordo asked again.

'Yeah, no problem. How many of you are there?'

'Eleven of us,' he replied, 'We'll be with you in a minute. We'll just get our gear out of the van, and we'll be there.'

Turning to Tony, I looked him in the eyes and motioned to the lot that had just turned up.

'I had to say that you two were my mates, otherwise they would have said . . .' I hesitated for a second and then continued, 'they'd have said, "Who the fuck are those two niggers?" or something like that.'

'I know,' replied Lewis quietly. 'Don't worry about it. It's cool.'

Once they had got their gear, and as we walked back towards the gate to where Alex and his crew were waiting, I chatted away to the lads who had just turned up and managed to avoid talking about the fact I was working with a couple of black guys, the conversation centring on people I hadn't seen for ages and about what they themselves were up to. Alex was sitting on the ground as we came into view. Approaching him with my mates, I could see by his face that he thought I had brought him a decent bit of business.

'Hello, boys,' he said, 'how many have we got here then? I'll do you a special rate seeing as there's a few of you.'

I cut in.

'This lot ain't paying. They're with me.'

'They *are* paying,' returned Alex, 'but I'll give them a good discount.'

Tony cut in.

'Hang on, Alex, they're his mates.'

Alex looked at Tony then at me, and, for a moment, I thought it might kick off. The Scousers were always ready for a scrap, and they would have loved the opportunity to batter a load of blacks, and, as half the guys who had been with Alex when Tony, Lewis and I left him were no longer there, there was a more than good chance they would have come out on top. Before anything could start, Jordo cut into the conversation.

'Could you use some gear? I've got someone inside who's sitting on a weight of top blow going cheap. He's brought it with him, but he can't be bothered to do it in. He's decided he wants to enjoy the weekend with his bird. I can sort you out if you fancy it . . .'

Alex looked at Jordo, at me, at Tony and Lewis and at my other mates who had just arrived. I don't know whether it was because he wanted to avoid a confrontation or he genuinely believed Jordo could do a deal with the puff he'd mentioned, but he let me stamp everybody up without charging them and motioned me to take them through. As we moved away from Alex and his crew, Shieldsy walked alongside of me.

'You alright there, Joe?' he said. 'Who the fuck are that lot?'

'Yeah,' I replied, 'I'm sweet. I'm just working with them to earn a dollar – that's all.'

'Stick with us, lad, we'll look after you,' said Jordo, joining in the conversation.

For a moment I considered it but then decided against their

offer and opted to go back to Alex and his crew to carry on work-ing. I was still hungry to earn more money, and they had my ultraviolet pen.

'Cheers, mate,' I replied. 'I'm OK. You lot have a good time, and I'll maybe see you later.'

Once we'd passed through the gate, I shook hands with them all, and, as they walked into the festival, I could see that they were buzzing from getting in, and I knew they would have a brilliant weekend. Again, I considered going with them, but, even though as I turned to go and rejoin the mob outside my heart missed a beat, I continued back in the direction of the exit gate and the yardies awaiting my return. Approaching the crew, Alex was giving me a really bad look.

'You and your friends think you're clever, don't you?' he demanded.

'How d'ya mean?' I replied.

'Your friend spinning me a line about getting me a weight of smoke and then getting in for nothing.'

In my peripheral vision, I could see both Tony and Lewis raise their eyes skyward as if they were saying to themselves, *There's no need for this*. I looked directly back at Alex.

'Listen, they're my pals. Why shouldn't I try to do them a favour? That's what we do. We're mates, and we stick together. Anyway, you're the one who let them in for nothing, and you never know, they might turn up with that smoke if we stay here long enough.'

The eyes of his crew turned on to Alex. Whatever he thought had happened, there was clear logic in what I was saying, and I got a sense that most of the people present had a degree of sym-pathy for me, albeit a miniscule amount, but no one could argue that it was Alex who had let my mates go in for free. He said nothing but instead gave a knowing nod and wagged his finger, intimating that he would be watching me more closely than ever.

Turning to Tony and Lewis before staring at me again, he barked, 'You three, back to work!'

Without looking at each other, but with each of us knowing what the other was thinking, the three of us began to scan the faces of the passing people, searching for the telling signs of those who had not got a ticket and were desperate to get into the festival.

We had been doing this for a couple of minutes when a girl approached me. At first I thought she might want to get in, but there was something not quite right with her body language, and, the closer she got, I thought I saw a look of concern in her eyes. Then I recognised that it was Ruby, the nurse living in Santa Monica who I'd taken through with her mates the previous night.

'Hey, what's up?'

'Lost my friends . . . I haven't seen them since last night, and I can't find my tent.'

I chuckled. I didn't mean to upset her any more than she already was, but I couldn't help it.

'It's not funny,' she said, the frustration in her voice clear and matching the look of concern on her face.

'Don't worry about it, lovely, you'll find them. You found me, didn't you?'

She cracked a slight smile.

'It's Ruby, isn't it? My name's Joe. We met last night when I got you and your mates in.'

'I remember.'

'Smoking?'

She let out a laugh, and her smile lit up her face.

'Go on then,' she said, grinning. 'Might as well . . .'

'You're a darling when you smile, you know.'

Doing her best not to smile now, she nevertheless half acknowledged the compliment as I motioned for her to sit down. Having momentarily forgotten the circumstances that had led me to this surprising but welcome chance meeting with Ruby, I was quickly reminded as I joined her on the grass at the side of the path. I glanced up to see a few of Alex's lot looking our way and smiling and no doubt passing lewd comments to each other about me and Ruby, but, to give them their due, Tony and Lewis moved away and left me to it while the rest of their crew were cool and let me crack on without her even realising they were with me.

As I rolled a joint for her and one for myself, Ruby explained that once she and her friends had left me the previous evening they had set up camp inside the festival boundaries and all gone out together without arranging a meeting point in case they became separated, but, as she laughingly admitted, even if they had done so, she probably wouldn't have been able to find it anyway. She thought they had made their camp near Gate 4 and had come out to see if there were any messages left for her among the many stuck to a part of the security fence away from the gate, and, from there, she'd made her way around to Gate 1 to where she'd seen me.

She was alright, Ruby. She was really pretty – just my type, in fact – and she was a cool chick to go with it, and, although she'd lost her friends, it was pretty clear she wasn't stupid. With the spliff relaxing her, she and I chatted about finding her mates before the subject turned to how we'd first met.

'Are you camped near Gate 3 then?' she asked innocently.

Looking at her and past her at the same time, I saw a couple of Alex's lot look our way and turn their heads so their ears could hone in on my reply, and I imagined that the others who were not in my line of vision but within earshot were also doing the same.

'No, mate,' I said quickly, hoping to sound casual enough to convince everyone who was tuning in, 'we're on the inside, right in the middle of it by the main stage.'

While I continued the conversation, quickly turning it to how many times I'd been to Glastonbury, the fact I'd got away with her inadvertently letting them know where I was camped was still in my mind as I tried to calculate whether the information would be any good to the crew or whether I had been imagining their apparent interest. Fortunately, it seemed as if those listening had swallowed what I'd said, and, temporarily forgetting the circumstances in which we had met, I focused in on how nice Ruby was.

She had blonde hair that was tied back in a pony-tail, which swung from side to side when she spoke, and her brown eyes, high cheek bones and extremely kissable lips gave her the appearance of a woman who could have easily been a model.

Although she was tall and slim, she was extremely well proportioned. She was dressed casually in a cheesecloth shirt and faded flared jeans, which gave her the appearance of a 1960s hippy. The more I looked at her and listened to her speak, the more I fancied her, my heart beating nineteen to the dozen.

Suddenly, my thoughts were interrupted by the same warning whistle I had heard when I'd escaped from my predicament on the Thursday night. Glancing up, I could see Tony and Lewis walking hurriedly towards the gate and out of sight, with the rest of Alex's crew looking like they were ready to move, and double-quick at that. Reacting myself, I half stood and leaned to my left to see what was going on, spotted what I knew had to be the problem.

Trotting right up the middle of the path, and now no more than two hundred yards away, were two of Her Majesty's mounted constabulary, and, being on horseback, they probably had a good view of everything ahead of them.

I looked back at Ruby, who hadn't yet quite caught on, and then over at Alex. He glared at me, pointing menacingly with his left forefinger while his right hand was tucked into the left inside pocket of his jacket.

As his lads looked to him to make a leadership decision and prepared themselves to do a runner, it dawned on Alex that he now had two prisoners. Staring at Alex, I motioned for him to stay down low and get in tight behind the cars that were parked along the side of the path.

Ruby and I had been sitting about six or seven feet away from a battered Ford Sierra, and, giving her a no-shit serious look, I whispered, 'Get in, quick.'

Following me, she, too, kept down and moved quickly to lie right in and almost underneath the left side of the motor, and, as I looked up the hill towards Alex, I could see that he and all those with him had followed suit. Even though the police were high up, I knew that if everyone stayed tight where they were, they wouldn't be able to see the other side and down low behind the parked cars and vans we were now using for cover.

'What's happening?' Ruby whispered, laughing, but with a hint of the trepidation she had when we'd met earlier returning to her voice.

'I'm working with these guys,' I replied, my glance causing her to turn her head to look at the bodies up the slope pressed to the ground behind the parked cars.

She looked at me again.

'OK then. I got nicked by these guys,' thinking as I spoke that the last thing a nurse needed was to get involved with the police. 'Kidnapped if you like, but it's too long a story to tell you now. Trust me, Ruby, you're safe with me, mate. Please, trust me.'

'Yeah, but why are we hiding?'

The thought had crossed my mind as well, even as I had taken the decision. I was thinking that I could have just as easily have stood up and walked on to the path, and, without even letting them know what was happening, used the police as my ticket to escape.

Unfortunately, my natural instincts had kicked in, and seeing the two uniforms had immediately made me want to hide, and, what with Alex having taking refuge with two of his boys just feet away, hiding behind a Volkswagen Camper and giving me a look that meant serious trouble, I realised I was right in it up to my neck.

That aside, the thought of a gang of people running at the first sight of the plod would have had the radios buzzing within seconds, and, being white among a group of black geezers, I would have stood out. Running down the slope would be going straight towards them, while trying to run up the hill and getting through the gate would have been equally futile. Alex was looking tense.

'Look, Ruby, it's probably 'cos they're carrying a bit of gear or something, but the thing is, those guys are trouble, and, if they think I'm going to bubble them to the plod, it could get nasty. They're tooled up.'

By this time, the horses were close, their hooves clattering on the stones and rocks of the track on which they were walking. Ruby stared me in the eyes, and I stared back. She let out a silent laugh, like a kid playing hide-and-seek. I laughed as well, easing the tension I was feeling, imagining my heart racing at double speed.

The horses were level with us now. I could just see enough of the track from under the car to make out their hooves, and, although they walked by in seconds, the time I held my breath extended to when the police were at least fifty yards away. Guiding the horses through the gate and into the festival, the two mounted officers didn't look back, and we were safe.

Everyone remained motionless until Alex made the first move. Taking on the manner of a platoon commander rallying his troops, he gathered his crew around him, and they crouched on their haunches waiting for instructions, save the two soldiers detailed to keep their eyes on me, who, very politely, insisted that we go with them.

'It's cool, bruv, it's cool,' said one.

I looked at Ruby and offered her my hand.

'Come on,' I laughed, 'we'll soon find your friends.'

With that we stood and, joining the others, made our way towards the gate and into the festival. Once through, Alex, who had been leading the party, hung back as his troops walked on and then waited for the others to join them once they were out of the immediate gaze of the stewards.

As I drew level, he joined me, and, with Ruby walking next to me on my left, he whispered a 'Well done' in my right ear and pressed something into my right palm. Gripping whatever it was and addressing him without looking his way, I turned to Ruby.

'She needs to find her mates.'

He looked at her as Ruby and I looked at him.

'She's safe with us,' he said.

I opened my hand to see what Alex had given me. It was an ecstasy tablet.

'What's this?' I said with an air of annoyance. 'This is no good to me.'

'Give it to your girlfriend,' Alex replied mockingly. 'She looks like she could do with cheering up.'

'I'm hungry,' I retorted. 'It's food I need, not drugs.'

Sneering at me and looking at Ruby, he replied, 'Eat her pussy.'

I stopped dead in my tracks, and, turning away from Ruby, I stared Alex in the face and gave him a look of sheer disgust.

'That's out of order. I don't care who or how many you've got wrapped around you, that was way below the belt.'

Alex just laughed and made his way to the front of the pack, and we were off again, making our way through the masses in snake-like single file with myself and Ruby at the back, save for the two detailed for guard duty trailing the pair of us. The further inside the festival we went, the denser the crowd became and the harder it became to keep pace with the people in front.

Irish band Hothouse Flowers had just finished their set, and many of the those who'd watched them were walking away from the Pyramid Stage, while those approaching the arena to watch Christy Moore, who was next on the bill, were coming in the opposite direction, meaning that the flow of human traffic was nothing less than congested. Sensing an opportunity for us to get away, I purposely began to hang back as much as I could without arousing the suspicion of our minders.

After a few minutes we were some twenty yards behind the guys in front of us, and, as we came to the bottom of the incline near the main stage where the main drag began, I knew the moment to get away had come. As Alex led the others to the left along Stage Road, I grabbed Ruby's hand and started walking hurriedly to the right and towards the crowds that were in front of the Pyramid Stage. Without looking to see if our two minders were following, we meandered our way between those waiting for the band to come on stage and headed in the direction of Gate 4 and as far away from our last sighting of Alex and the main body of his crew as possible. Once we had got to the far side of the field, but remaining within the mass of people, we stopped, and, after checking that we hadn't been followed, I motioned to Ruby to sit down.

'What was that about?' she demanded. 'I thought you said you were working with those guys, but it looked heavy, and you didn't say why, and then you said they had kidnapped you. Now we're away from them, I think you should tell me all about it.'

'Wanna stick one?' I said, throwing her the puff, skins, cigarettes and my lighter.

She smiled and laughed.

'Yeah, OK,' she said, 'but I want you to tell me exactly what you've been up to.'

I sighed.

'OK then, it's like this . . .'

She sat there silently, taking in my account of what had happened to me over the last few days, giving me her full attention and only appearing to break her concentration when she needed to relight her spliff.

'What do you think then?' I asked, as I finished my tale at the point when I had met her outside Gate 1 earlier that afternoon.

She exhaled, and, looking deep into my eyes, nodded, her manner suggesting not so much that she was impressed with what I had told her but rather that I had enjoyed a lucky escape and was fortunate to be alive.

'You're a lucky boy,' she said.

'I must be, 'cos I met you . . .'

The smile returned, replacing the furrowed look she'd had when she was listening to my story.

'Are you hungry?' I asked. 'I know I am. Shall we go and get something to eat and then we can go and look for your friends.'

'Sounds good to me, but I haven't got any money.'

'That's OK, Gate 4 is just over there,' I said, pointing in its general direction. 'My mate is looking after some money for me. We'll walk over, pick it up and grab some food.'

As we prepared to leave, I stood up first and offered my hand to Ruby. Accepting it, once she had got to her feet, she linked her arm through mine, and, as a couple, we made our way to Gate 4 where, hopefully, Pat would be waiting with the £250 I had left with him. Even though I'd managed to slot about £60 from working the stamp with Alex, I wanted to grab the money I had given Pat. He was there, and after he'd passed me the cash, and following a brief exchange in which I assured him that I was OK, Ruby and I headed off into the festival to get something to eat and drink. Hopefully for Ruby we'd find her friends, but, seeing as she was still content to have her arm linked with mine, and every now and again I could feel her body pressing against me, with any luck it wouldn't be too soon.

CHAPTER SIXTEEN

We walked back along the track from Gate 4 and then on past the main stage to the catering outlets on Stage Road before we stopped for a rest, some food and a spliff. Ruby was well alright and everything I fancied in a girl. She seemed independent and able to stand on her own two feet. She was a little bit sassy, and, despite having only been in her company for a short time, I was nothing less than smitten, and it seemed as if she was getting prettier every time I looked at her. She was a festival girl, into a smoke and a few long weekends away at bashes like Glastonbury and, the more I considered it, the thought of her in a nurse's uniform was a definite plus. I had the feeling that she liked me, at least a little, and, best of all, despite the fact that she lived in the States, she was unattached with no one waiting for her.

We sat on a bench in front of one of the food stalls and watched the throng of people passing us by and chatted away, both of us seemingly putting our troubles to the back of our minds. However, with the sun beginning to fade and the twilight approaching fast, Ruby's thoughts again turned to the friends she'd come to Glastonbury with and, perhaps more importantly for her, where – if she didn't find them – she would stay over the coming night.

'Come on then, Ruby, let's go and try to find your mates. Where can you remember being with them?'

'Well,' she replied, 'I think we parked our car near to where we saw your friend Pat, but I couldn't find it. I was hoping the others would have had left a note for me on the car just in case they thought I'd decide to go back to it to look for them. After that, I started walking around the outside. I don't know why, I suppose it was because I panicked. That's when I met you again.'

'Yeah, but, do you know what, I think you're getting muddled up. I first met you over by Gate 3, which is on the other side of the festival. You're miles away.'

'I'm sure it's this way.'

She was insistent, so I went along with her, and we walked back towards Gate 4, and, once we'd gone through it, we turned left and started walking along by the perimeter fence. It was made with horizontal slats of concrete, was about fifteen feet high and there were two watchtowers spaced four hundred yards or so apart, obviously sited there to ward off anyone who tried to scale the barrier. There were cars and vans parked a few yards away to our right with the fence on our left, and together they formed the path we were now following.

Even though I had seen it from a distance, its relevance hadn't occurred to me, but as we neared the car that was parked right next to the fence, it was patently obvious why it was there. Unfortunately for its owner, someone had smashed the driver's side quarter-light window, leaned in, broken the steering lock and pushed the car up to the fence, using it as a step-up to enable them to clamber over and into the festival. Judging by the dents in the bonnet and the roof, the car had been there for several hours, if not days, and plenty of people had taken advantage of this means of entry.

With it still being Saturday, the owner was probably blissfully unaware of the state of the car and would be until the end of the festival. With that in mind, I had no problem in opening the door and sitting in the driver's seat, gesturing to Ruby that she should join me on the passenger side. We each rolled a joint and chatted away, passing the time while enjoying a smoke. We'd been there for about ten minutes when three guys came into view, following the route we'd just taken.

'Looks like we could be in business,' I said.

As the trio approached the car, I stepped out and acknowledged their presence.

'Alright, lads? Do you want in?'

'Yeah, that's right.'

'That'll be a tenner. That's a tenner each . . .'

They looked at me first and then at each other.

'Why should we give you that?'

'Well, number one, it's my car, and, number two, you'll need me to give you a bunk up and over. It's quite a height, and you'll never do it on your own.'

They looked at each other again.

'Twenty.'

'Make it £25, and you've got a deal.'

They were happy with that, and, after handing over their money, they each in turn stepped up on the bonnet and then on to the roof before I cupped my hands, allowed them to place a foot in them, and then lifted so their chest was level with the top of the fence. Once that high, they were able to pull themselves up on to the top and make the drop down to the other side and into the festival. With the business completed and the three guys safely in, I turned to Ruby and gave her £15.

'What's that for?' she asked.

'Compensation.'

'Compensation? For what?'

'For losing your mates. You'll be able to put that towards buying them a drink when you link up again.'

She didn't argue, and I wasn't bothered about giving her something. After all, she'd helped in as much as she had been my look-out as I assisted the punters' illegal entry. We returned to our seats in the car and were rolling another spliff when I saw a couple walking towards us, each wearing a rucksack and looking like they had yet to get into the festival. I turned to Ruby.

'Looks like we could be busy.'

We both got out of the car, and, after negotiating a fee of £10 each, the pair were soon pushed up, over and in.

'Good 'ere, innit?' I said to Ruby.

She laughed, saying nothing but seemingly acknowledging the fact that she was happy doing what we were doing – at least for the time being.

After being at 'our car' for about an hour and a half, even I was surprised at how much money we'd made. Considering that it was Saturday evening, with only one full day of the festivities left, after getting another ten people in we had earned £135 between us. Three more potential customers were approaching from our right, having obviously spotted the car. I got out of the motor as they got closer.

'You looking to get in?'

'Yeah, that's right,' replied one of them in a deep Brummie accent, 'but what's it to you?'

'Well, you'll need to get on the roof of this car if you're going to get in over the fence, and the thing is, it's my motor.'

'And?' enquired another of the three.

'And,' I replied, 'it'll cost you a tenner each.'

The third of the trio spoke.

'Why should we give you £10 to get over the fence? We'll just climb up and over.'

'You'll need a lift, mate. Trust me. I've been doing this all weekend. The fence is still too high to get over without someone pushing you up, even if you stand on the roof of the car.'

The three looked at each other, and, although they reluctantly agreed to the £30 it would cost them for my assistance, I had the feeling they would try to mug me off and get in without paying.

'Step up,' I said, motioning them to stand on the bonnet and then the roof.

The first guy got up, and, as I linked the fingers of my hands and cupped them, he lifted his foot, and I hoisted him high enough to enable him to get his arms over the top of the fence and haul himself up. As he balanced on top of the barrier, the second one climbed up on to the car.

'Go on then, pal, give me lift up,' he demanded.

'Let's see your money first,' I replied.

Glancing at his friend who was still on the ground and then up at his mate who was on top of the fence, he pulled a wad of notes out of his pocket, separated three £10 notes and showed them to me.

'You'll get this when were all up there.'

'OK,' I replied, but even though I agreed to his terms, I was still wary.

I lifted the second guy, but this time with the assistance of his mate, who helped to haul him up while sitting on the top of the fence. As the third one got on to the roof of the car, I saw him give a triumphant smile to his two friends, who were now both precariously balancing on the top of the fence and waiting for him to join them.

'The money . . .' I said, looking up at the one who had shown me the cash.

'When you've lifted him up,' he replied, again showing me the notes and motioning to his mate on the roof of the car.

As I began to lift the third guy, his two friends, now sitting astride the fence, leaned down and, lowering a hand each, grabbed him by his wrists and began to pull.

'The money!' I repeated, this time with an air of annoyance, as I could see what was going to happen.

The one with the money, starting to laugh at me, replied, 'Fuck off, ya prick.'

Not panicking, I looked up at him, grabbed his friend's legs and put enough weight on them to prevent the two on the fence from being able to lift him the last few feet.

'The money!' I demanded.

'Let him go, you fucking idiot,' came the reply.

'You want him in, I want paying.'

'Fuck off,' he said again.

Putting more weight on to the third guy's legs, I again asked for my money, but this time increased the ante by shouting, 'Security! Security!'

'Pay him up,' shouted the guy whose lower legs I was holding. He was looking and sounding distressed, obviously not wanting to be left on the outside by his two friends who, if they wished, could have ditched him and dropped down to the other side of the fence and gone into the festival.

'Help! Security!' I shouted again, as the guy I was holding down desperately tried to kick me away, but the more he tried, the tighter I held on.

'Give him the money, Stew. Please, or I ain't gonna get in.'

Realising that if I didn't let go and kept on shouting his mate would not be joining them, Stew gave me a disparaging look and threw the money towards Ruby. Looking at me and then at the three Brummies, she smiled as she picked it up and, with that, I let his friend go and watched, laughing, as he was eventually lifted up by his two friends, the three of them jumping down to the ground on the other side of the fence and disappearing from view.

I jumped down from the roof of the car and joined Ruby on the ground. It must have been a release of days of pent-up tension, because my sides were literally aching as I laughed, so much so that I thought I'd never stop, although I eventually collapsed on the ground. The sight of me almost rolling around in a fit of the giggles made Ruby respond in a likewise manner. What anyone would have thought if they had seen the pair of us I don't know, but we didn't care, and it seemed like minutes before we both managed to stop. Eventually, we regained our composure, although as we began to stand up, intermittent bursts of laughter affected us both.

Once we'd recovered, we got back in the car and smoked

another joint. We sat there chatting, comfortable in each other's company and learning a little about each other's life. I was hoping that I'd be able to see her once the festival had finished, but she told me that she'd have to be back in London on the Sunday evening whether she found her friends or not, as her flight back to America departed from Gatwick on Monday afternoon. There was a pen in the pocket of the driver's door, and, using the cover of an AA book lying on top of the dashboard, we wrote down and exchanged our telephone numbers and addresses.

It wasn't long before three more for an 'over the fence' entry were helped in, their fee contributing to what had become a profitable evening's work. By 9.30pm we'd made a total of £235 between us and decided to call it a day. Having left the car and walking back along the fence, another two likely customers came towards us, heading towards the spot where we had been working. Instinctively, I turned to say something, but Ruby tugged my arm, and, as I looked at her, she gave me a slight shake of her head. I knew that she'd had enough and was again thinking of trying to find the friends she had lost.

As we entered the festival through Gate 4, I looked for Pat, but he wasn't there, so both Ruby and I continued towards the main stage and the Stage Road that lay beyond. As we made our way through the crowds in front of the Pyramid Stage, the evening's main act, in the shape of Lenny Kravitz, was on, and, stopping to listen to a few numbers, we involuntarily started to hold hands like a couple of regular lovebirds. Even though I was content standing next to Ruby and sneaking glances at her as we both watched the band, hunger got the better of us both, and we picked our way through those in front of the stage and went to the other side where the main part of the Stage Road drag began. Stopping at the first row of food stalls, we divided the money we'd made, with Ruby pocketing £130 and me taking the rest.

While she joined one of the queues to buy a burger, I walked down a bit to a get vegetarian meal. By the time I went back to find Ruby, she was in company, chatting excitedly to three girls. These were the friends she'd been looking for, and, by chance, they had been coming down to the main stage area and had spotted her buying herself a meal.

'Hey, Joe, I've found my friends,' said Ruby as I approached.

'Hiya, we've been looking everywhere for you lot. Where have you been?' I said by way of an introduction.

After spending a few minutes chatting, Ruby took my hand and led me a few feet away from where her friends were standing.

'Thanks for looking after me,' she said, squeezing my hand tightly. 'I've had a great time with you. I owe you, big time.'

'You owe me nothing. I'm glad you've found your mates. Just make sure you don't lose each other again.'

She took my other hand and, standing straight in front of me, leaned forward and kissed me on the lips.

'Don't lose my number, will you,' she said.

'Of course I won't. And don't you lose mine.'

She looked me in the eyes.

'Call me when you get home? Please.'

I smiled back at her.

'OK, I'll call you.'

'Promise?'

'Yeah, I promise.'

I put my hands on her hips and, pulling her forward, returned the kiss she'd given me moments earlier. We hugged each other and kissed again before we let each other go.

'Take care, Ruby, it's been brilliant meeting you.'

'You, too, Joe. Call me.'

'I'll call you.'

She turned and walked towards her friends. As she reached them, she looked back and blew me a kiss.

'Take care, you lot,' I called, staring straight at Ruby.

She smiled, and her friends waved, and I stood there watching them walk into the crowds of people and disappear.

As I thought about Ruby leaving me alone, Alex and his crew flooded back into my mind, and I suddenly became alert to the fact that I might be spotted. Even though it was now dark, the light from the traders' stalls and burger vans lit up the drag, making those within a few feet visible to everyone who passed. Keeping my head down, and having decided to head for my tent and the safety of our camp, I made my way into the middle of the drag and started back towards Gate 3. However, by the time I reached the Meeting Point junction that led up to the Green Fields, I'd changed my mind, reasoning that there would be nobody at our camp, and they would, instead, be out and about enjoying the festival.

Turning right, I walked towards the Green Fields, which was somewhere I reckoned Alex and his boys would not be interested in visiting, considering that their main source of business – selling Es and cocaine – would be taking place in and around one of the entry gates or in a field where there was a rave.

The further from the main drag I went, the more relaxed I felt. Although I could occasionally hear the sound of what was happening in the main area, it was the sound of whoever was on the Jazz Stage to my left that came to the fore, but as I passed it and made my way into the Green Fields further up the drag, it was the noise of the occasional wind-chime or some weird oriental-type tune that was prominent, the music giving a mystical feel to the tents, tepees and stalls located there.

In total contrast to the main drag, the stalls and cafés were, in the main, selling vegetarian and wholefood, and, as ever, the majority of people were more chilled out than their compatriots in the rest of Glastonbury and, outwardly at least, appeared to be more experienced in the art of attending festivals.

I entered a café called The Cat In The Hat, which had a picture of the character in the well-known Dr Seuss books on the A-board outside, and bought myself a cup of tea. Finding an empty corner of the marquee I sat on the ground and built a spliff. Having been on the move for most of the day, running around for Alex and then grafting with Ruby, I found the peaceful atmosphere of the café totally relaxing, and, coupled with the calming effect of the joint, I felt totally at ease. I felt my eyes getting heavy and had an over-whelming desire to doze off. Stretching out, I pulled one of the bean bags that were on the ground closer to me to use as a pillow, got myself into a comfortable position and drifted off into a much-needed sleep.

By the time I opened my eyes, the café was nearly empty, save for a few people who, like me, had decided to crash where they were. The counter serving food and drink was still open, and, after buying a cup of tea to wake myself up, I rolled a joint, smoked it and left the marquee that had been my temporary bedroom.

It was now 2.30am, and, what with the sky being clear, the temperature was decidedly chilly. I pulled my jacket tighter to my body as the night air caused me to shiver. I hadn't been walking for too long when I came across a few people sitting around a campfire. Without saying anything, but acknowledging their presence as they did mine, I sat down a few feet away from the burning embers to enjoy the benefit of the warmth they were giving off.

It was one of the sides of the Glastonbury Festival that I really enjoyed. Like-minded, decent people who were content to live and let live, allowing others to come and go without any hassle or malice, without even requiring a explanation or excuse to sit and join the company they were in.

It might well have been the middle of the night, but there were still thousands of people about and lots going on. Even though it was quiet where I was sitting, the hum of activity from the festival was still audible, albeit in the background. In an hour or so, people would start making their way towards the Stone Circle. The appearance of the sun, gradually creeping over the hill of Ridgy Ground on the eastern side of the festival, would be accompanied by the beat of drums and bongos and the whoops and cheers of those who'd stayed awake to watch the phenomenon. It was something that mankind had been observing since time immemorial, and it somehow gave me, and I'm sure many others who were there to see the sunrise, a sense of what my ancient ancestors might have felt when the dark and cool of the night was replaced by the reassuring light and warmth of the day.

I decided to stay up and watch the sunrise. A slow walk back to my tent would take me fifteen or twenty minutes, and by then the night would begin to give way to the first strands of light of the coming day. I hadn't seen much of the festival this year on account of my working the stamp and earning some extremely good money, and while I wasn't bothered about missing the bands and the revelry in favour of an unexpected but very welcome income, I still wanted to return home with a feeling of having taken part. Being at the Stone Circle with the sun worshipers on the last full day of the festival and seeing that bright ball of orange come up over the horizon fitted the bill.

I headed back to The Cat In The Hat for another cup of tea and the accompanying spliff, and, before too long, it was time to follow those heading up the slope of the drag towards the Stones. By the time I reached them, there must have been at least two thousand people there, a large number of which were travellers. Many people I knew were wary of these guys, but I felt comfortable in and around the lot that were at the Stones, even though I was, by their standards, a total conformist and a part of normal, everyday society.

Watching the travellers, I felt somewhat envious of their lifestyle, a mode of being that saw them going from festival to festival over the course of the summer and then retiring to Wales and the remoter parts of the country to see out the winter.

It was they who were creating the atmosphere at the Stone

Circle, with the sound of their percussion adding to the air of anticipation and excitement that was building as the dawn approached. Groups were sitting around fires they had built to keep themselves warm enough to see the night through, and, as I had done earlier, I found a space in a circle of people watching the flickering flames and the glow of the burning wood.

Having gained the benefit of the fire's warmth, I then went and sat at the top of the hill overlooking the Stones and the festival. As I had done every time I'd visited this part of the grounds, I gazed across to the hill opposite and towards the camping area where Gruff, H, Billy and the rest of my friends were staying, with the valley housing the events below and to my left. It was amazing to think that there were in the region of 80,000 people crammed into such a small space.

I thought about what everyone at our camp would be doing and guessed that in all probability they would be sleeping. When they woke, they would rise with the knowledge that it was the last day of the festival, and I wondered if, like me, they would have more than a touch of regret as they reflected that the next day it would be back to town life and a sharp dose of reality.

I was thinking about my mates but was content being in my own company. One way or another, I'd spent much of my life alone, and it was something that I was used to. I could think for myself with no one there to interrupt whatever train I was following. Sometimes it seemed to make things easier. That's how I felt at that moment anyway. I was well happy that, after the past couple of days I'd had in the company of Alex and his cronies, I was still in one piece and was more than buzzing with the thought of the money I'd made.

The eastern sky was starting to get lighter by the minute, the darkness being replaced by the grey of the first glimpse of dawn. It wouldn't be long before the sun would rise above the hill and begin to shine down on Glastonbury. Despite the few hours' sleep

I'd snatched earlier, I was beginning to feel tired and wished that the sunrise would come more quickly than it was doing.

It was nearly 4.30am and time to roll another joint, this one in honour of the daybreak. By now the spliffs I was consuming were helping me to stay awake, the habit of smoking them down to the roach ensuring that my eyes would remain open. However, with the drummers beating their instruments with more intensity and the people around me infused with energy as the sun began to appear, I, too, tasted the excitement that was in the air and didn't really need a stimulant.

A few minutes later the sun was up and throwing its rays down on the festival site. Leaving the party in full swing, I retreated from the Stones and made my way down the dusty path towards Babylon and, having reached the main drag, turned right towards Gate 3, making my way in the direction of the home that was my tent at our campsite.

I had exited the gate and was going across the lane towards the hill opposite, which would take me to my tent when, to my left, I was aware of a group of people coming in my direction. As I turned to look at them, I realised it was some of Alex's crew, but it was too late for me to turn away or even run for it, and within a second or so I was surrounded.

Stopping me in the middle of the path and without saying a word, one of them started to frisk me, and, after putting his hand into the front pockets of my jeans, he extracted the loose change and a £10 note, the money quickly disappearing into his jacket pocket. Even though I'd been collared and had been mugged again, I felt fortunate that the money I'd collected from Pat and had made from working the car was stashed in my money-belt and, as such, remained undiscovered as I was patted down.

Even though it seemed I'd been captured for the third time, the search seemed only half-hearted, and I sensed that I wasn't in as much bother as I had been on the two previous occasions. When

I'd been given the once-over, the one who'd taken the money and the three he was with left and walked on.

A second later, as more black faces came into view, I saw Carlton and knew that he would – should he also want to search me – look in my money-belt, having seen it previously. The ones who'd searched me had left me alone in the lane, ready for the second wave of their crew to do what they wanted with me. Turning around, so my back was facing Carlton, I quickly put my hands down the front of my jeans, undid the zip to my money-belt and pulled out the folded wad of banknotes, slipping them into the front pocket of my jeans before turning again to face the crew who were now no more than thirty yards away. Moments later Carlton and a couple of the others were standing face to face with me.

'You checked this one out?' he called, looking down the lane in the direction of his mates who'd just been through my pockets.

'He's clean,' shouted the one who had taken the money out of my jeans, and, as he laughed, he patted one of his own pockets.

'Here,' said Carlton, motioning me to stand directly in front of him.

I did as I was instructed, and, as I did so, he put a finger inside the waist of my Levi's and hooked out the strap to my money-belt.

'Take it off and open it,' he demanded.

'Skint, mate,' I said, removing and opening the belt. 'Your mate's just taken my last few pennies.'

He inspected the money-belt and stared at me disparagingly. He said nothing as I looked stone-faced and straight back at him. His eyes narrowed, and for a split second I thought that he would root through my pockets, but that wasn't in his mind as he dropped my money-belt on to the ground and walked on.

As I stooped to pick it up, I was expecting a boot or a bat to come crashing into my head or body, but nothing happened, and the rest of the crew followed Carlton up the lane and away from where I was still standing.

I thought that was that, but then I saw Duane, and, seeing me, his hand slipped into his jacket, and he drew his knife. Extending his arm, he started to walk slowly towards me with his blade pointing in my direction. He was ten feet away from me when, seemingly from out of nowhere, Lewis and Tony appeared.

'What the fuck are you doing?' screamed Tony as he put his hand on Duane's left shoulder and stopped him coming on to me.

Duane swung around and pointed the knife at Tony.

'Try it, you prick, and see what happens . . .' Lewis said slowly, causing Duane to turn away from Tony and look at him.

At that, Duane seemed unsure as to what to do next, then he turned and again tried to move towards me but was pulled back by Tony.

'Leave it, you fucking idiot. Don't you think you've seen enough of that this weekend?' said Tony, who was now holding Duane by his shirt collar and pushing his clenched fist into his throat.

Suddenly, Duane didn't look quite the man he thought he was, and, rather timidly, he put his knife back inside his jacket before he was pushed away from me by Tony.

'Walk away, Joe, now!' said Lewis, his eyes focusing on Duane as Tony again grabbed him by the collar and pulled him up the lane in the direction the others had gone.

I exhaled a deep breath of relief as I watched them follow the path taken by the rest of their boys, each step taking them further and further away from me.

Once again, I'd been extremely lucky, and I said a silent prayer of gratitude that I'd escaped relatively unscathed. The one who'd taken the money from my pockets thought he'd done well, but it was me who was inwardly laughing at him and his mates for missing out on the tidy sum now secreted in my pocket. Keeping calm, I moved to the side of the lane and stood there and began to roll a joint, the robbers again having allowed me to keep my gear.

I waited until they'd walked up the incline and were out of

sight then stayed a few minutes longer just to make sure they were gone, and it was only when I was positive that they wouldn't return and follow me that I moved and headed up the hill towards my tent. It took me five minutes to get back, and as I went I kept my hand on the outside of my pocket, feeling the notes inside as my stomach churned.

Reaching the field in which I was staying, I looked behind me, and, confident that I hadn't been followed, I made my way towards my tent. Even though I was fully alert and my natural instinct was telling me that I should be awake, I clambered into my canvas shelter, unzipped my sleeping bag and, once inside, had no other thought but to sleep.

CHAPTER SEVENTEEN

It was 10.30am when I opened my eyes. Totally refreshed from the sleep I'd grabbed, I got up straight away, had a wash and was soon dressed. Gruff and his lot were nowhere to be seen, so I looked into Billy's tent. He was out for the count, so I left him sleeping.

Returning to my tent, I sat inside and counted the cash I had on me. There was £380 in £5, £10 and £20 notes, and I again reflected on how lucky I'd been to get away from the yardies in one piece and with the money. Despite what had happened just a few hours previously, my desire to take as much home with me as possible was still overwhelming, so I left the money hidden under my tent until I could find H and give it to her for safe-keeping, save for £80 which I kept to spend.

Even though the total I had accumulated was an unbelievable bonus, I was gutted that I wouldn't be able to make any more. I had money on my brain and wanted to carry on, but because Sunday was a free day there would be no more to be earned by getting people in.

I decided to get a breakfast and to chill out for the rest of the day, take in as much of the remaining hours of the festival as I could. With midday rapidly approaching and an empty blue sky, the sun was making for a temperature in the late twenties, and by the time I'd walked to the drag leading up to the Green Fields I was sweating.

I bought myself a cold breakfast of muesli and a fruit smoothie and sat in the shade with my back to the wall of one of the stalls. Even at a place like Glastonbury, you could tell it was a Sunday.

There was an almost sedate pace about the people who were making their way up and down the drags. Mind you, the heat and the fact that most of them had been busy enjoying themselves all weekend probably had something to do with it. Even so, there was still a buzz about the place, with people seemingly determined to make the most of the last day of the festivities.

There was plenty to do and loads that I could have seen, but I was happy sitting there watching the festival crowd going to and fro, and I could easily have stayed there all day. I had enough puff to last me and a few bob in my pocket, and I was, to all intents and purposes, sorted.

I knew that I was doing myself some good just sitting there and relaxing. I'd been on the go for what felt like weeks, even though it was only a matter of a few days, and, although I was doing nothing physical, my mind seemed as if it was still in overdrive with thoughts of this, that and the other racing about inside my head. I definitely needed the rest, and the sit-down was beneficial, even though it felt like my legs were stiffening up with the inactivity, the toil of my previous exertions beginning to take its toll.

After an hour or so I decided to make a move and head back towards the camp. I hadn't seen any of the others for a day or so, and I especially wanted to see H to give her the rest of the money I'd stashed when I left my tent earlier.

Making my way through the festival and back out of Gate 3, I started up the hill towards our campsite. Many of those who had been trading by the side of the drag were starting to pack up and go, and as I walked slowly up the incline I noticed a guy loading cardboard crates of bottled water into the back of a Transit box van.

'Hello, mate,' I said, pointing at the water. 'Is any of that for sale?'

'What you after?' came the reply.

'How much for a carton of the water?' I replied.

The man looked at his goods.

'I'll do you a crate for a tenner,' he said, turning to face me.

'How many have you got?'

'Twenty-four bottles in a crate.'

'Cartons,' I retorted.

He turned again and looked inside the back of his van.

'There's eight left.'

'I'll give you £40 for the lot . . . if that's any good to you?'

He looked at me and then into his van before turning back to me.

'OK, you've got a deal. What you gonna do about taking them off me?'

'How long do think you'll be here for?' I asked.

'Another hour or so.'

'OK then, here's £20. I'll take two crates with me now, and I'll be back shortly for the rest. Is that alright with you?'

He replied that it was, and I took the cartons and carried them up towards my campsite. As I walked away with the first part of my purchase, my head was busy with the calculations – 24 x 8 = 192 x £1 = £192. The £40 I had paid meant a profit of £152 if I sold every one of them at £1 each.

Reaching my tent, I glanced over to see if the motorbike man was about. I was in luck.

'Hey, you OK?' I enquired.

'Hi, man,' he replied. 'Had a good weekend?'

'Top. You busy?'

After explaining that I wanted him to give me a lift the short distance to where the rest of the water was and then back to my tent, he said it was no problem. We drove down to the van, picked up the other six crates, paid the man the balance and, sitting on the back of the bike with the water placed between myself and the driver, headed up the hill to the camp. Once there, I left four crates next to my tent and got a lift with the other four down to the main stage. I was dropped off about a third of the way back along Hen-house Lane, the drag that connected the Stage Road with the top of the hill where hundreds of people had decided to camp and have a view of the Pyramid Stage, a place I thought ideal to punt my wares. I told my taxi man that I would wait for him where he'd left me, and he drove up to my tent to collect the remaining crates of water.

I had only been there a matter of seconds when I got my first customer.

'Is that water for sale?'

'Yes, mate, a pound a bottle.'

'Three please.'

'Cheers, mate.'

The sun was now belting down with a vengeance and making for some thirsty people. While the water I was selling wasn't ice-cold, it wasn't yet warm, and because it must have been stored in a fridge before I bought it, it was cool enough to satisfy those who were asking.

By the time the motorbike man turned up with the other four crates, I'd sold two and a half of the first lot. Giving the motorbiker £20 for his trouble, he left me to my own devices. I watched him as he carefully weaved his way through the crowds down to Stage Road, until he turned to the left and was out of sight. Then it was back to work.

An hour or so later I only had two crates left, so I began to walk through the crowd waiting for Van Morrison to take the stage, and, in no time at all, I'd sold out and was gutted I had no more bottles. The water had, to coin a phrase, sold like hot cakes, and I'm sure that if I'd have had another eight or so crates of it I would have sold them easily. As it was, I had cleared £135 profit and was satisfied with that.

I would put £100 with my savings and keep the £35 to spend. What with the remaining money I had left after breakfast, I had about £80 to get some food and generally fritter away. It would easily last me the rest of the day, and I'd be going home with nearly £3,500. I'd had a good weekend.

Leaving the main stage area, I visited a couple of the stalls on the Stage Road drag to change the pound coins I had for notes, and, once I had £140 in folding, I put £100 in my money-belt and kept the rest to hand in the pocket of my jeans.

With no more money to make I had an overwhelming desire to relax, so headed back up towards the Green Fields where the mood would be chilled and laid back. Once there, it was back to The Cat In The Hat, where I bought a meal and a drink and contentedly sat by the edge of the drag and spent a couple of hours soaking up the sun and picking up some of the peaceful vibes emanating from the hippies and the extremely nice and well-meaning folk populating the immediate location.

Feeling refreshed, I left the tranquillity of where I'd rested and began to make my way down towards Babylon. As I reached the Meeting Point, I turned right and headed up towards Gate 3. I still hadn't spent any quality time with anyone that I'd gone to the festival with, and I felt like seeing a friendly face.

I had just about reached the approach to Gate 3 when I met Gruff and H coming in the opposite direction, making their way towards the main stage. I decided to walk with them, and, as we passed through the crowds, I gave H the £100 I'd put aside from selling the water and told her where I had put the £300 I'd hidden at our camp so she could put it into safe-keeping for me.

As we chatted about the weekend's events, the conversation turned to the money I'd made and the activities of the scallywags and grafters who'd been so prominent outside the gate entrances.

'We told you about what happened to those two brothers, didn't we?' asked H.

'Yeah, you did. Have you heard any more?'

'It was a couple of travellers,' Gruff answered. 'They got stabbed up and battered by a gang of blacks in one of the lanes outside Gate 3. One of them is meant to be in a really bad way.'

'Oh, yeah. And when was that?'

'The rumours going around say it was late on Thursday night. I heard it was an argument about them not paying to get through a hole under the fence,' said H.

I was stunned. Alex and his lot certainly fitted the bill for the people who committed this violence.

'Sure it's not a rumour?' I replied, my mind racing while a tremor seemed to shake my body, my legs going weak and causing me to miss a step.

'You OK?' asked Gruff, sounding concerned and looking at me square in the face and deep into my eyes, as though he was trying to see into my soul. For a moment, I'm sure he thought that I'd had something to do with it.

'Yeah . . . I'm OK.'

In truth, what Gruff and H had told me had shaken me up no end, and a few things that I'd noticed about the demeanour of Alex and his crew that I couldn't fathom at the time now fell into place. I knew that they'd been involved in some kind of bother on the Thursday night. I had witnessed the start of that, and if it was Alex and his crew who did do these two guys over, I realised why they had suddenly appeared so nervous and on edge on the Saturday. I could see why they had panicked when they saw the mounted police coming towards them outside Gate 1.

I also knew that I had been extremely lucky to get away without getting shanked or even shot myself, and even luckier to get away with the money that I'd made. That crew had a palpable streak of evil running through them, which showed in the way they acted and bullied people, and, Tony and Lewis apart, I felt that I was right to brand them as nothing better than low-down scumbags.

My heart skipped a beat as I thought about my encounter with them and how lucky I had been. I said a silent prayer of thanks to Jesus Christ for my deliverance from harm at the hands of Alex and his number and at the same time hoped that they would get their come-uppance at the hands of the Avon and Somerset Constabulary or, better still, another firm who would batter them senseless.

'You sure you're alright?' said H. 'You look like you've seen a ghost.'

'I'm OK,' I repeated. 'I'm gonna get myself a drink. I've gone dry. You two carry on, and I'll see you later.'

I didn't tell Gruff or H about what had happened to me or, in particular, who I had met because I didn't want to mess their festival up. Even though it was the last full day and we were leaving in the morning, any trouble that I had been in, been associated with or even near would have put a dampener on proceedings as far as they were concerned. They were a nice couple, straight as a die, lived clean lives and avoided trouble like the plague. They'd been good enough to allow Billy and myself to travel to the festival and to camp with them, and H had been brilliant in looking after my money without asking too many questions, and I didn't want them to think that I had abused their hospitality.

More than that, if I had brought trouble to their door there was no way that they'd consider me coming with them again, and, although I had loads of other mates at Glastonbury that I could travel with in the future, there was a certain safety in going with them that was somehow comforting and which also helped keep my feet firmly on the ground.

The thought of Alex capturing me again sent a chill down my spine and mentally put me right back on my toes. Not that I wasn't in the first place, but now there was a sense of fear firmly in my mind. As I tried to reason with myself that everything would be alright, I found some comfort in the fact that I only had £80 or so on me, and, if I was caught and turned over by Alex and his men, they wouldn't get that much from me compared with what I'd given H to look after.

Nevertheless, I couldn't get the memory of when I had first encountered Alex from my head. That initial realisation that I was in deep trouble, on my own, and not knowing whether I'd find myself with some nasty injuries or even dead haunted me again. There again, I thought, if I stay with the crowds I should be safe.

I could hear myself saying it out loud and then, from somewhere inside me, came another voice. Fuck them. Don't let them ruin your day. I agreed. With my mind made up to enjoy what time was left, I made my way towards the main stage to try to see if I could find anyone I knew.

I couldn't, so I again headed up towards the Green Fields, this time via the NME Stage where, later, The Lemonheads would be entertaining the crowds, continuing up and along the old railway track that ran along through the land on which the festival was being staged. The trickle of revellers who were in the process of leaving in the morning had by now, in the early evening, become a flowing stream.

A lot of people walking the drag had their rucksacks on their backs and were carrying their kit and heading for the exits, and, although there were thousands who wouldn't be leaving until Monday, the festival seemed a lot less busy than it had been on the Friday and Saturday, and yet the buzz around the place was brilliant, with those staying until the Monday morning getting set for a chilled-out and crowd-free evening. But it was the last night, and the thought of leaving gave me a feeling like I used to get when I was a kid, when it was the last day of the summer holidays and it was back to school the next day. This would be my sixth night at Glastonbury, but the time had flashed by. I had been here since Tuesday, and it seemed like everything had merged into one long day and night.

The drags were busy, the stallholders were doing a roaring trade and the music of the bands and sound systems was prominent. Glastonbury was still rocking.

I chuckled to myself as I watched a couple of girls struggling with their luggage, the weight of the tents and sleeping bags they were trying to carry not helped by the fold-away chairs and too many clothes in their rucksacks. Their baggage caused them to stop and look totally helpless as they realised they still had a long way to go to just reach an exit and then find their car or get on a coach.

I felt sorry for them as they stood there right in the middle of the drag, needing a hand with their stuff, but no one was going to stop and help. Somehow or other they would make it home, even if it meant ditching some of the stuff they were carrying. It might involve a fair bit of sweat, a few tears and, judging by the face of the taller of the two, some cross words between them, but they would get there in the end.

I spent the rest of the evening on a slow wander around the fields up in the green areas where the hardcore and long-time travellers and hippies had their buses, vans and tepees, their cafés and stalls. I always found it almost magical that within the boundaries of the festival there were places like this that the majority either didn't know about or simply chose to ignore.

Among the travellers and hippies were people who'd probably been at the first festival held at Worthy Farm, and they were more than likely on their second or third week on the site.

The people who had gathered in this particular area were the older, pre-New-Age type of traveller, and I was happy staying among them for the rest of the evening. A soothing atmosphere hung like a welcoming glow, and I remained deep into the night. By the time I eventually got back to the camp, dawn was breaking, and, when I retired to my tent, I was relaxed and happy.

I slept until 9am, when I was woken by the general hubbub outside. Looking out of my tent, I could see that the noise came from the majority of the people in our field breaking down their camps. After getting washed and dressed and packing my bags, I went to see Gruff to find out what time we were leaving.

'Twelve o'clock sharp,' he said. 'You have a good one last night?'

'Yeah, not bad. I've had a top few days.'

'So, what was it that turned you sick when me and H saw you yesterday?'

'Took a whitey.'

'What was it?' Gruff repeated, not believing what I said about feeling faint.

I looked him in the eye.

'I'll tell you all about it one day.'

'OK then. How much money did you make?'

I half sighed, half laughed.

'Just over three and a half . . . That's what I'm taking home anyway.'

The look of disbelief on his face was soon replaced with a concerned expression and a slow shake of the head that had *You're fucking mental* written all over it.

I winked at him and turned to go back to my tent. As I walked past Billy's, I stopped.

'Get up!'

There was no response. I stooped down to open the tent and peered inside. Although lying in his sleeping bag, he was awake.

'We're leaving at twelve. You'd better start getting up.'

He just lay there, staring at the roof of his tent.

'Billy,' I said, frustrated at his lack of response. 'We're leaving at twelve.'

'Right . . .' he mumbled, not shifting his stare.

'Get up,' I repeated before I turned and went back to my tent and started taking it down.

Half an hour later I'd packed my tent and put it inside the

Transit with the rest of my gear and was ready to go. I put my head into Billy's tent. He was still lying half comatose.

'What are you doing?'

He didn't move.

'What you doing?' I repeated. 'Gruff and them are gonna be going in an hour or so. I ain't helping pack your stuff away. I've done my bit.'

'I'm just taking my clothes,' said Billy, the tone of his voice suggesting he was less than happy. 'Fuck the tent and all.'

I didn't bother rising to that one. I'd known him long enough to know when an argument was going to start, so, if he wanted to ditch all his gear and have to worry about getting new stuff the next time around, that was up to him.

'Are you getting up?'

'Aye. Ten more minutes.'

I stepped back out of his tent and walked over to the others, who were dismantling the rest of the encampment and getting everything ready to be loaded up for the journey home. Billy was like a spoiled kid sometimes, and today I knew he was going to have a major tantrum, the thought of him kicking off edging my frustration level up a notch. I had bought him a ticket, brought him to the festival with a nice bunch of people who'd gone out their way to look after him, I'd earned him a proper few quid and even looked after him again out of my money that night I'd carried on grafting after he'd fucked off.

'Hiya,' H said, smiling. 'You two getting ready?'

'Yeah,' I said, temporarily forgetting Billy and reminding myself that I was now in the company of H, Gruff and the others. 'My kit is by the van, and Billy will be half an hour. That alright?'

'No probs,' she replied.

'Any chance of a quick word?'

H knew I wanted my cash and motioned for me to follow her to the cab of the van. We sat inside, and she gave me the money and wouldn't take any off me for her trouble, but she finally accepted £30 towards the petrol back to Dorset where I'd pick up my car.

'Is Billy going to be ready?' she asked as she left me alone to recount my money.

'If he's not he'll miss his lift.'

She didn't bother replying, shut the van door behind her as I used the passenger seat as a desk and divided the notes into their various denominations and recounted the cash. It was the biggest wad of notes I'd had in my hands for quite some time, and the buzz I got just from feeling the money was brilliant. I would be able to pay off my debts as soon as I got home, have a holiday and put some away for the next rainy day. I felt great. Having put the money into my bag, which I then transferred into the back of the Transit with the rest of my kit, I left the van and went to see if Billy was getting ready to leave. When I looked inside his tent, he was still lying in the same position, apparently not having moved since the last time I'd tried to rouse him.

'Billy! Get up!' I shouted.

He was beginning to really get on my nerves. Billy didn't move.

'Are you gonna fucking get up or what? The others are almost ready to go now, and they won't want to have to wait for you.'

'Fuck them,' he said, screwing up his face as if to emphasise his words.

'Why are you being like this?' I demanded. 'They've been good enough to bring us here and look after us, and the least you can do is show them some respect and be ready for when they want to go.'

'I've got sunstroke,' he replied feebly, looking for some kind of sympathy.

'So, what you saying? Everything's got to stop because you're not well? Get up, or we'll go without you.'

There was an unopened can of Coca Cola lying at my feet. I picked it up and offered it to him.

'Here, drink this. It will wake you up.'

'Fuck off.'

'Listen you, ya fuckin' prick, fuckin' get up.'

For a moment, I thought that my shouting at him had done the trick, as he sat up, but instead of accepting the drink and making a move to rise, he lay back down and rested on his elbows.

'You're the fucking prick,' he shouted back at me. 'I saw you getting had off by those coons on the Thursday and was laughing at you. Did you think I'd try to come and help you out?'

At this I snapped and the can went flying and would have hit Billy right in the face had he not moved quickly enough. I felt like steaming into him and smashing him with my fists but managed to retain my composure and stepped back out of his tent and walked over towards H's van.

The others had already loaded their kit on to the Transit and were ready to go.

'You OK?' I asked as I approached. 'I'm ready.'

'What about Billy?' said Gruff, giving me a look that made me think that he'd heard us arguing.

'He's staying here,' I replied quietly. 'He's going straight home with one of his mates.'

Gruff gave H a sideways glance, shrugged his shoulders and we all boarded the Transit. I sat behind the driver's seat on a ledge that covered the rear wheel arch from where I could see out of the driver's window. As we drove away to join the queue of vehicles leaving Glastonbury, I caught a sight of Billy's tent in the offside mirror, but didn't give the selfish Scottish cunt a second thought.

We had been driving for about ten minutes and were in the main stream of traffic when Gruff – who was driving – turned his head to catch my attention.

'You haven't got any gear on you, have you?' he asked.

'Nothing,' I lied.

I had about a quarter of hash in my pocket, which would, should the need arise, be quickly transferred into my mouth and swallowed, but as I looked down the road ahead I could see the reason for his concern. In the distance were two police Range Rovers, and it appeared that we were approaching a police check-point. As we got closer, it looked as though the officers had pulled a car over and were in the process of searching the occupants.

When we were almost there, I saw who the police were questioning. It was Alex, Carlton, Delroy and Duane. My heart skipped a beat, and I shrunk back behind the front seat so they wouldn't see me, but there was nothing to worry about. They were more concerned about what was happening to them than who was driving past. As our van drew level, I adjusted my position so I could get a good view of things from the mirror on the left-hand door. It looked like they were being nicked, and there was but a single thought in my mind – Fucking nice one!

We had been driving for another four or five minutes when, out of the front window, I saw Tony and Lewis. As the van passed, it seemed to me that they were on their own and, with rucksacks on their backs, like they were leaving.

'Pull over a minute, Gruff, please,' I shouted. 'I need a word with someone I've just seen. I won't be long, I promise . . .'

Gruff stopped the van at the side of the road, and I jumped out of the back.

'Hey,' I shouted. 'What's happening?'

'We're on the way home, mate,' said Tony.

'I think I've just seen a few of your lot getting nicked back there,' I replied, hoping that I hadn't been mistaken in assuming the pair were on their own.

'Nothing to do with us, bruv,' Lewis replied. 'We're finished with them guys.'

'Nothing to do with me, I hope,' I said quickly, fearing they had fallen out with Alex and the rest of the crew as a result of sticking up for me on the Saturday night in the lane when Duane had come at me with the knife .

'No, Joe, fuck all to do with you,' Tony retorted. 'That cunt Alex fucked us off for the money that he said we'd earn. If he's been pinched by the rozzers, I can't say I'm sorry.'

'Wait there one minute,' I said, turning and walking back to the van.

As I opened the rear door of the Transit, and before anyone could say anything, I looked at Gruff and said, 'Thirty more seconds, please . . .'

I reached into my bag and found my wad of cash. It was divided into £100 folds and I peeled off fifteen of them. Exiting the van, I walked the short distance to where Tony and Lewis were waiting.

'Here. Take this for your sister's kid,' I said, handing the cash to Tony. 'Thanks for helping me out the other night. I mean that.'

The look on their faces was that of shock. Whether it was because they didn't think I'd earned that much, or because they were wondering how I'd got away without the money being found by Alex, I don't know, but I could tell they were humbled and genuinely grateful for my donation towards the child's fund. They were still speechless as the van's horn sounded.

'I've got to go,' I said, offering my hand and shaking theirs in friendship. 'Take care, and try to stay away from those fuckers.'

'Joe . . . What can I say?' Tony mumbled, a tear running down his cheek.

'Don't worry,' I said, looking at the pair of them. Smiling, as I turned to make my way to the van, I added, 'Easy come, easy go.'

Back on board, I made myself comfortable and contemplated the fact that I'd just given away £1,500. Fuck it, I thought, I'll earn that back next year.

Before long, I'd drifted off to sleep. We were back at Gruff and

H's house within an hour and a half, and, after transferring my kit from their van to my car, I said my goodbyes and thanks to them and drove the hundred or so miles back to my home in Devon.

I was just a few minutes away from my place when I saw Billy's girlfriend walking along the street. She waved at me to stop, and I pulled the car over to the side of the road.

'Where's Billy?' she asked. 'Have you dropped him at home?'

'He's stayed up there. He was on about getting a lift with someone else. Not back yet then?'

A stern expression appeared on her face.

'No, he's not.'

All I could do was give her a sympathetic look. Although I'd parked on the side of the road, my car was blocking the path of the drivers behind me, and one of them had sounded his horn.

'I've got to go,' I said, somewhat weakly. 'Tell him I'll see him later . . .'

With that, I pushed the gear stick into first, pulled away and drove the short distance to my flat. That evening I did a bit of running around, returning some money I owed to a few of my mates and paying my pot dealer the considerable debt I'd accrued then spent the rest of the night at home getting stoned and reliving every moment of the last seven days at Glastonbury.

The following evening my phone rang. It was Ruby calling from the States. She told me that she and her friends had made the long journey from Somerset back to Santa Monica and had arrived safely and in one piece. With the pleasantries out of the way, we chatted for about an hour, both of us wishing that we were in each other's company. There was no doubt about it, we had feelings for each other, and it was obvious we wanted to meet up again and take our short, but nonetheless sweet, relationship further than we'd had the chance to do at Glastonbury.

*

The next morning, my debts now cleared, I went into town and put £1,000 into my bank account, keeping the rest of the cash I'd made to hand. Opposite the bank was a travel agency, and, after crossing the road, I entered and approached a girl behind one of the desks.

'Can I help you, sir?' she politely asked.

'Yes please. I want a return to Los Angeles.'

'When would you like to travel?'

'The day after tomorrow would be lovely, if there's a flight available.'

'Let's see what I can find for you . . .'

LONDON BOOKS

FLYING THE FLAG FOR
FREE-THINKING LITERATURE

www.london-books.co.uk

PLEASE VISIT OUR WEBSITE FOR

- Current and forthcoming books
  - Author and title profiles
    - Events and news
  - Secure on-line bookshop
- Recommendations and links
- An alternative view of London literature

London Classics

The Angel And The Cuckoo *Gerald Kersh*
Doctor Of The Lost *Simon Blumenfeld*
The Gilt Kid *James Curtis*
It Always Rains On Sunday *Arthur La Bern*
Jew Boy *Simon Blumenfeld*
May Day *John Sommerfield*
Night And The City *Gerald Kersh*
A Start In Life *Alan Sillitoe*
There Ain't No Justice *James Curtis*
They Drive By Night *James Curtis*
Wide Boys Never Work *Robert Westerby*

MALAYAN SWING

PETE HAYNES

Aidan is different. He is small, awkward and often silent, an easy
man to ignore, mock or exploit, yet on the inside he is intelligent
and thoughtful. He speaks to the reader in a way he can't manage in
everyday life, reflecting on the world around him with great insight
and an almost childlike honesty. This is the internal life of an outsider.

We meet Aidan not long after he has moved into a room in a
shared flat, forced from the home in which he felt secure by a policy
labelled 'care in the community'. But the community is dismissive and
threatening. He becomes lonely and scared, his best friend
the radio he carries everywhere. An old shed offers a hideaway
during the day, while his evenings are often spent in the local pubs.

Aidan's physical and mental state starts to deteriorate, and when
he bumps into Joey from the home he comes to the notice of some
bad people. He wanders the streets and is attacked, his life quickly
spiralling out of control. The story ends in dramatic fashion, but it is
Aidan's decency and a sense of escape that remain with the reader.
Malayan Swing is a moving novel, a testament to those living on the
margins of society, and as such is a brave and important work.

London Books
£8.99 paperback
ISBN 978-0-9551851-6-8
www.london-books.co.uk

London Classics

MAY DAY

JOHN SOMMERFIELD

Set across a three-day period in 1930s London, *May Day* follows
the fortunes of a wide range of characters as working-class anger
bubbles over in the East End and spills towards the West End on
May 1st. Idealism, exploitation and police violence all play a part
in the journey from cockney London to moneyed London,
the climactic demonstration highlighting a period of
heightened social awareness in the capital.

First published in 1936, *May Day* is an imaginative, fast-paced
book that rejects stereotypes as it searches for the common
humanity in every individual. From the hardships and dreams of
factory workers to the privilege and regrets of the wealthy, author
John Sommerfield brings a whole society into the spotlight.
Sommerfield was a politically active man who fought in the
Spanish Civil War and on the streets of London, and his writing
reflects both his beliefs and his own positive nature.

London Books
£11.99 hardback
ISBN 978-0-9551851-8-2
www.london-books.co.uk

London Classics

DOCTOR OF THE LOST

SIMON BLUMENFELD

When young Thomas Barnardo arrived in London in 1866, he planned to study at the London Hospital before venturing abroad to work as a missionary. The conditions he found in the East End stopped him in his tracks. Unemployment, poverty, overcrowding, alcoholism and deathly diseases were bad enough, but seeing thousands of half-starved children living on the streets broke his heart. Inside a year Dr Barnardo had opened the ragged-school Hope Place and by 1870 the first of his eponymous homes was in operation. His work continues to this day. *Doctor Of The Lost* is the fictionalised story of Tom Barnardo's early years in East London.

Author Simon Blumenfeld grew up in the same streets, his cult 1935 novel *Jew Boy* capturing the magic of the Jewish East End of the 1930s, and *Doctor Of The Lost* (1938) recreates the area in Dr Barnardo's day. Drawing on a friendship with his widow, Blumenfeld brings Barnardo vividly to life, showing the struggles he faced and the battles won. *Doctor Of The Lost* is set in a London of rampant industrialisation, when the few became rich at the expense of the many, and yet this was also a period of charity and good works, when idealists such as Thomas Barnardo were prepared to stand tall and fight back.

London Books
£11.99 hardback
ISBN 978-0-9568155-2-1
www.london-books.co.uk

LONDON CLASSICS

THEY DRIVE BY NIGHT

JAMES CURTIS

When he discovers the body of a murdered girlfriend, former
convict and small-time crook Shorty Mathews panics and heads
for the Great North Road, leaving London behind as he enters
a world of bustling transport caffs, canny lorry drivers and
happy-go-lucky tarts. A manhunt is soon launched, Shorty
hitching rides as he tries to stay ahead of the police, along the
way saving a travelling girl from being raped. Decency and
romance are alive and well, while back in London the real
murderer is busy prowling the streets of the West End,
his mental ramblings promising further killings.

They Drive By Night is a fast-paced, slang-sharp,
socially-aware novel that sees author James Curtis developing
themes previously explored in his first London Classics
release *The Gilt Kid*. Curtis captures both the vibrancy and
realities of the lorry-driving world and life on the streets of
1930s London, while at the same time highlighting the
murderous contempt some people felt towards those
they considered below them in society's pecking order.

London Books
£11.99 hardback
ISBN 978-0-9551851-4-4
www.london-books.co.uk